Gratitude Sidekick
Journal

*You already have everything you need
to be happy.*

Created with love by
Amir Atighehchi, Ari Banayan, & Mikey Ahdoot

For information about permission to reproduce elections from this book, email team@habitnest.com
Visit our website at www.HabitNest.com

PUBLISHER'S DISCLAIMER

While the publisher and author have used their best efforts in preparing this book, they make no representations or warranties with respect to the accuracy or completeness of the contents of this book. The advice and strategies contained herein may not be suitable for your situation. You should consult with a professional where appropriate. Neither the publisher nor the author shall be liable for any loss of profit or any other commercial damages, including but not limited to special, incidental, consequential, or other damages.

The company, product, and service names used in this book are for identification purposes only. All trademarks and registered trademarks are the property of their respective owners.

SPECIAL THANKS

We'd like to extend a wholehearted, sincere thank you to Skyler Wolpert and Lindsay McDermott for formatting + editing help. We love ya!

ISBN: 9781950045068

FIRST EDITION

The Habit Nest Mission

We are a team of people **obsessed with taking ACTION** and **learning new things** as quickly as possible.

We love finding the **fastest, most effective ways** to build a new skill, then **systemizing that process for others.**

With building new habits, we empathize with others every step of the way *because we go through the same process ourselves.* We live and breathe everything in our company.

We use our hard-earned intuition to outline **beautifully designed, intuitive products** to help people live **happier, more fulfilled lives.**

Everything we create comes with a mix of **bite-sized information, strategy, and accountability.** This hands you a simple yet **drastically effective roadmap** to build **any skill** or habit with.

We take this a step further by diving into **published scientific studies,** the opinions of subject-matter **experts,** and the **feedback we get from customers** to further enhance all the products we create.

Ultimately, Habit Nest is a **practical, action-oriented startup** aimed at helping others take back decisional authority over every action they take. We're here to help people live **wholesome, rewarding lives** at the **brink of their potential!**

– Amir Atighehchi, Ari Banayan, & Mikey Ahdoot
Cofounders of Habit Nest

Table of Contents

Our Mission in Creating This Journal

The truth of the matter is most people need some form of guidance when it comes to personal development.

Because you bought this journal, you're probably someone who is generally into personal development. You're probably familiar with ordinary journals that promise to help you remain productive, create useful routines, etc.

Let's be real.

Most journals have the same jargon and setup on every single page, and after looking at a simple cloned page that you've seen for a week straight, you become desensitized.

This journal is a compilation of the best tips and strategies discovered by people who understood the importance of practicing gratitude on a daily basis. We've dug through tons of books, podcasts, scientific studies behind willpower and motivation, cool products/apps/gadgets, and dissected the best strategies to find the golden nuggets of info and present them here.

Our team spent countless hours researching:

1. How making a practice of gratitude affects our lives, both on a day to day basis and in the long term.
2. Which gratitude practices actually foster a sense of appreciation on a consistent basis.

3. What factors lead to amazing relationships and how we can value our relationships in a way that helps us remember the significance and beauty of what we have.

The result is a journal bringing something new to the table. **Actionable tips** and **motivating content** are what we're all about.

Every day, for 66 days, we're going to give you the information, motivation, and accountability you need to stay consistent in making significant strides towards your goal of bettering yourself.

Why 66 days? In a recent study on human behavior, researcher Phillippa Lally discovered that on average, it takes 66 days to form a habit. In reality, there is no exact, definite, magical moment. But from personal experience, 66 days is a long enough time to build the habit so strongly that you can tap into it at any future point in your life.

You are building a life-altering habit here that you can use at any moment in your future. The beauty about this is by diving head first into mastering your mornings, you'll immediately start seeing the benefits on day ONE.

<u>Our mission is to be your book-sized personal trainer for building this life-altering habit into your day to day life.</u>

In this moment, you're already doing something amazing. The fact that you're reading this means somewhere in you there is a burning desire to really add this habit and make it stick.

Let's make it stick and add value to our lives in an amazing, indescribable way.

The 'Why'

Why Gratitude Matters

One of the biggest hurdles we all face towards living a happy life is our tendency to focus on what is lacking and ignore the immensity of what we have to be thankful for.

No matter who you are, where you're from, and what your circumstances are, you have much more to be grateful for than unhappy about.

The emotions we experience are not dependent on the circumstances of our lives. *They are a result of the way we perceive our circumstances.*

Intentionally fostering a perspective of gratitude and optimism as often as possible literally changes the way you think so that over-time your initial outlook on things is one of positive emotion rather than negative thinking.

It *always* feels better to be grateful than it does to have a pessimistic perspective. And when we're feeling grateful and happy, we affect others positively, we're more creative, we're better problem-solvers, and we simply enjoy life more.

This journal is all about altering the mindset to focus on what we have to be grateful for on a consistent basis so we can enhance the quality of our day-to-day experience.

How A Practice of Gratitude Changes Our Lives

There are a host of benefits that come with creating an intentional practice of gratitude.

People who practice gratitude:

- Feel better about their lives
- Are more optimistic about the future
- Report fewer health problems
- Experience heightened satisfaction in their relationships
- Have an increased sense of resilience in the face of stressful life events
- Discover an enhanced ability to empathize with others
- Reduce the experience of toxic emotions
- Sleep better
- Experience improved self-esteem

When you truly, genuinely feel grateful every day, it shifts your whole perspective on life.

You start appreciating the little things on a consistent basis. Your mindset shifts away from the negative and toward the positive.

And the best part is, after practicing gratitude daily, over time this becomes your default state. You are physically rewiring how your brain works.

What You Stand To Gain

Everything.

You will undoubtedly encounter a completely renewed perspective on what is truly important in life. You'll gain the ability to consistently place value on what is important each day.

Appreciation and gratitude are fundamental emotions that we ordinarily take as reactions to positive circumstances.

Here's the thing - by practicing gratitude rather than simply awaiting its arrival, we in effect, *become* it.

When gratitude becomes a core aspect of who we are, everything in our lives begins to take the form of beauty.

Fostering this gift and beginning your gratitude practice can lead to a fundamental transcendence of the way you approach life. This can provide you with a sense of stable and positive love, admiration, and value.

When we transcend our perspective and begin to see life from the viewpoint of gratitude, our behaviors in response to the events and circumstances in our lives adjust accordingly. What happens after that can only be described as a rippling effect that we hope lasts forever. You quite literally become a ray of gratitude, spreading and shining its light on the world around you.

The Greater Good Science Center

The University of California Berkeley has created an interdisciplinary research center (Greater Good Science Center) devoted to the scientific understanding of individual happiness, compassion, strong social bonding, and altruistic behavior. They greatly focus their research and publishing on the origins, impact, and importance of gratitude.

The Greater Good Science Center is directed and was founded by Dacher Keltner. For the past 30 years, Keltner has been studying human emotions, starting with micro-movements of facial muscles to compassion, altruism, and empathy. His recent studies have been more focused on the relationship between powerlessness and health outcomes.

The Center publishes an online magazine related to all things well-being, ranging from topics like big ideas, community, culture, education, media and tech, mind and body, parenting and family, spirituality, society, relationships, and workplace. They also have a podcast hosted by Dacher Keltner called 'The Science of Happiness, teaching research-tested strategies for a happier, more meaningful life.

Much of the research for this journal has come from articles published through the Greater Good Science Center.

Some Gratitude Research

Before making a change in your life, it is always helpful to have some background information. For that reason, we're going to take a moment to delve into some of the research on gratitude and explain what humanity really knows about gratitude from a scientific perspective.

While reading this, it's important to understand and remember that gratitude research is a relatively new phenomenon, and that it's always extremely difficult to have concrete evidence about what is essentially a personal experience for each of us.

Research suggests that gratitude is not merely a construct of society or culture. Rather, gratitude is in some way embedded in our DNA and evolutionary history.

One of the interesting reasons for this belief is that other animals besides human beings engage in what two of the leading gratitude researchers in the world, Robert Emmons and Michael McCullough, call "reciprocal altruism activities."

This means that animals do things for other members of their species as a way to earn favors later on, which scientists believe is an expression of gratitude.

Primates have also been studied in relation to gratitude. For example, chimpanzees are more likely to share food with a chimpanzee who groomed them earlier in the day.

Neuroscientists have identified specific areas of the human brain involved in both experiencing and expressing gratitude, and some studies have even identified specific genes that potentially underlie our ability to experience gratitude.

The Hedonic Treadmill

The Hedonic Treadmill is the observed tendency of humans to have a stable, set level of happiness that isn't drastically affected by huge positive or negative events that take place in our lives.

Basically, we exist at a general level of happiness, regardless of the circumstances.

As we earn more money, have more in our lives, chase and create abundance in whatever form we believe will satisfy us, our happiness levels don't actually rise very much and soon return to an ordinary stable level.

The idea behind the treadmill is that we're basically walking endlessly to remain in the same place in terms of our happiness. Because we think that there's something we're chasing in the external world that we believe will make us happy, we're endlessly walking on this treadmill that is, in fact, moving nowhere in terms of happiness.

The way to get off the treadmill, or to stop walking so quickly and wasting energy, is to change your perspective and values, shift your attention from what you're lacking to what you already have.

That doesn't mean you stop working towards goals, but you shift your perspective so that you enjoy and value every part of the process rather than saving your happiness and gratitude for what you expect to gain out of meeting your goals.

Why Gratitude Positively Impacts Health

Earlier, we listed a myriad of benefits associated with feeling grateful. It's a pretty incredible phenomenon if you think about it - how you feel about and perceive your life's circumstances changes your experience of them on SO many levels.

Some of the reasons gratitude may play a role in physical, mental and emotional well-being:

1. Prevents hedonic adaptation

Gratitude prevents us from taking positive improvements in our lives for granted. Rather than feeling happy for a few minutes when something amazing happens, intentionally being grateful for it allows us to savor it more. It helps us maximize the appreciation we have for great things that happen in our lives.

2. Builds positive action and emotion

Positive emotions can change the way we think and act. When we're happy, we're more adventurous, we're willing to try new things, push our comfort zone, and in a very real way, being happy changes our idea of who we are. This process provides us with more internal psychological resources that we can rely on in difficult times in our lives. It changes how we take the difficult periods in life.

3. Cancels out the physical effects of negative emotions

We're really only beginning to understand the physical and psychological impacts of negative emotions. Gratitude helps fight negative emotional processes that underly a wide array of physical and psychological disorders. Here's how it works: Essentially, positive emotions are incompatible with negative emotions and experiences. So, the positive emotions lessen the attention paid to the negative information from the outside world. The change in perspective and shift of attention can "undo" the effects of negative emotions.

4. Motivates self-improvement

Feeling grateful puts people in a state of mind in which their actions become increasingly positive towards themselves and others. The more people work to improve themselves, the more grateful they begin to feel, and the more they feel they have to be grateful for. It's a giant, wonderful self-fulfilling prophecy. Gratitude also cultivates other virtues like patience, humility and wisdom.

These are just some of the research-based reasons for gratitude affecting our health and well-being. Note: You can find a list of some of these sources at the end of this journal in the "How Was This Journal Created?" section.

The Overarching Impact of Gratitude

There are always things to be unhappy about - both in our personal lives and in the status of the entire world and humanity as a whole.

You've probably heard that in order to change the world, we first need to change ourselves.

For just a moment, think about how that makes *total* sense.

We don't even know how deeply impacted we are by our parents or other primary caregivers…. How deeply impacted we are by the people around us… How deeply we impact the people around us with our emotions, our story.

Who we are shows up in what we do.

What we do IS who we are.

And what we do is wholly dependent on how we live our lives and our situation / circumstances that show up.

If we were to learn to have a grateful disposition in our personal lives, not only would WE personally get much more out of life, we'd stop chasing some idea of happiness and simply be happy, but we'd also be teaching future generations how to value and respond to things in their lives in a much happier, healthier way.

Our children learn from what we do and how we are, not simply from what we tell them. The same goes for how we learn from each other. We read right through each other's lies.

We can't fake gratitude and positivity. But we can train ourselves, through understanding how valuable it is, to have a grateful disposition more often.

We can train ourselves not to take small things so seriously, not to take other people personally, and to give everybody some slack when it seems like they need it rather than judge everyone for the way they are.

Our learning to be grateful in our personal lives will have an impact on the world around us beyond simply feeling great about our own lives.

Understanding Your Why

As humans, what sets us apart from other animals is our desire to be great as opposed to simply surviving. We all have a vision of what our ideal life might look like.

The absolute most important aspect of changing your life for the better is… **Knowing your damn *Why*.**

The thing is, when we forget (and we forget quite often) the reason we're struggling to improve our lives, we tend to retreat to our habitual selves - to the person we were before we made the decision to change.

Having a clear understanding of your 'why' (what you want to change and why you want to change it) is what pulls you through the tough times you will inevitably face when altering your habits.

Here are a few simple questions that **you should take your time to answer sincerely before moving on**.

These questions are aimed at getting to the root of what drives you, why you bought this journal and what you expect to gain from using it.

If you're going to even make an attempt at this, you better know why you're doing it in the first place.

Seriously. Take the time to define your goal.

1. What do I imagine my life would look like if I intentionally practiced gratitude for the next 30 days?

_Happier with less attention
to the outside world and
others._

2. What sort of ripple effect would focusing on gratitude every day have on other areas of my life? On the lives of people around me?

_Nicer to be around. A
better mother and friend._

_____

_____

_____

3. What would my life look like if I do not do this? What
would I be missing out on? How would missing those make
me feel?

*My life would be dull.
I would miss my daily
communications - especially
the daily calls from Jayline
and Jim.*

_____

Bonus Question: What is the biggest thing holding me back
from using this journal and making a genuine attempt at
practicing gratitude for the next 66 days?

*Probably laziness and lack
of commitment to me and
making my life better.*

_____

_____

Bookmark this section and flip back here the next time
you're struggling to stay consistent with this habit.

This section is your SOS Lifeline.

The 'Who'

The Three Factors of Behavior Change

James Clear, author of *Atomic Habits*, writes that there are essentially three parts to behavior change (we love your work, James!).

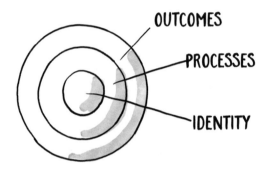

1. The Outcomes

The first is the outside layer: The Outcomes. This is synonymous with your goals (e.g. I want to be happier and more appreciative of my life).

Outcomes are most useful at setting a larger, over-arching vision for where you want to go to. The downsides of over-focusing on your outcomes are relying on hitting your goals to bring you happiness instead of enjoying the process, and a lack of practicality for what to do day-to-day.

Your outcomes are likely to change over the course of your life to match your ever-evolving goals and needs.

2. The Processes

The second, middle layer, is about processes — this boils down to what system and action steps you put in place to allow your outcomes to come to fruition. These are things like: *I will practice thinking of a few things I'm thankful for every day/ The next time I get stressed, I will take step back and shift my view on what I'm dealing with to better serve my life/ I will tell 2 people how much I appreciate them today.* Processes are synonymous with strategies and tactics.

These can be very useful, especially when you find one that clicks, and you'll see a number for you to experiment with, sprinkled throughout the journal.

These processes are likely to change over time as you test them out. See what works best for you and switch things up when you get bored / desensitized to them.

3a. Your Identity

This one's the big kahuna. This is the inner-most layer, identifying what your internal belief is of yourself as a person. The biggest mistake people make in enacting behavior change is placing way too large of a focus on the first two parts of this puzzle, while entirely forgetting about the third and the most impactful — how you view yourself.

By properly emphasizing WHO you want to grow into, you will maximize your self-respect, satisfaction, and ability to control your actions — more than any motivation or strategy can give you. Your identity is what you can always fall back to set your intuition, to guide you to what you should really be doing.

An example of setting your identity is:

"I'm someone who masters my perception of every event in my life. I will lead a life where I own my emotions, where I practice unbelievable gratitude for my ability to LIVE, especially when things get hard."

*After defining the identity you want to grow into for yourself, chances are this will **not change much**, but rather, only **strengthen over time** based on your actions.*

3b. Your Identity on Your Off-Days

As much as this plays a role in building towards your goals, it's equally as important in regards to times where you fall off the wagon.

Most people subconsciously forget about what their self-identity looks like when this happens, allowing a massive negative self-view to kick in.

This leads to a major emotional factor, *guilt*, to kick in, and as many studies have shown, **guilt is a willpower destroyer** (these are cited at the end of the book).

Instead, mindfully set your identity in these situations…

Grow into the person who uses every opportunity of falling off-track to further strengthen your ability to *switch from your off-days back to being on-track.*

Chances are, you won't live life from a perspective of gratitude, every single day, for the rest of your life, right? Life is about knowing which habits to employ, at the right time, to help you get the most fulfillment out of life.

This involves testing different things and seeing how they serve your life's purpose. In order to really do this, you must master the ability to switch back and forth and discover how to quickly rebuild the momentum you had with your habits, without any guilt that you 'lost your mojo.'

Be the type of person who can forgive yourself for your mistakes, who will love yourself unconditionally, and be a true best friend to yourself (because if you can't, who will?).

We know these are big emphases on emotional states that can come off as 'fluffy' but the truth is our fulfillment in life directly ties to our emotional states. Learning how to master them is the true feet of this journal, not just building up a specific habit.

Establishing Your Identity

Write your identity statements below.

What kind of person do you want to grow into through this process?

_A kind, caring person
using each day to end
with a feeling of good
will._

What kind of person do you want to be when you fall off the wagon of your habits? What do you want to remember about who you are and how you can repurpose these days to serve your life?

_Remember the kind of
person I set out to be
and make daily small
efforts to regain that person_

The 'What'

Phases of Building a New Habit

The development of building a habit happens in stages. There's science behind all kinds of different theories about the stages that come along with altering habits, and here's what we found is the most accurate.

Days 1-7, Hell Week.

…This is going to be tough.
It's going to be tough because you're rewiring a lifetime habit to be totally different. Expect yourself to resist the habit. Your'e not going to want to take the time and energy to find a new perspective and really think deeply about being grateful for all that you have in your life.

But don't worry, this will all fade. Guaranteed. It will fade because you will begin to find things you're so sincerely grateful for, that you'll have no choice but to feel the raw emotion of it. Once you start to feel the strength and love that comes with feeling grateful, you'll start WANTING to fill out the journal every day.

But for your brain and body to adapt, you must take action. You must distrust the challenging thoughts and resistance your brain will naturally give and show it what you want it to adapt to.

Daily challenge prompts in the journal will give you specific actions to stay focused on while affirmations will set the tone for the direction your life is headed in.

Days 8-21, Staying Consistent.

The good news is that after you've gotten through the first week, you've begun to build momentum. Your brain is beginning to understand the change you're making and how focusing on gratitude impacts your days. Seeing the benefits of your new practice will carry you.

The key here is to find a strong sense of consistency. Sometimes we become satisfied at the first sign of progress and we think everything has changed and our job is done. If that happens, don't trust it! You have to struggle to stay consistent.

During this period, a kick of inspiration can make all the difference. Developing habits takes time and just because you've taken a big first step doesn't mean you're off the hook. You'll be getting daily challenges to keep you motivated, new expert strategies, and different ways to help you think and incorporate gratitude into as much of your life as possible.

Days 22 - 66, *Hardwiring - Retaining Interest In Your Personal Improvement.*

Once you've passed phase 2, you're well on your way to becoming a gratitude junkie! It's amazing. All it takes is just about a month to incorporate gratitude as a daily practice (something you think about and act on every day), but that doesn't mean that phase 3 isn't crucial, because it is.

To build a habit means to fundamentally change something about the way you are. You'll know how beneficial this new habit is, you'll look forward to doing it many days, and when you forget to be grateful, you'll see a drastic difference in how you perceive events.

During Phase 3 you'll get really cool and interesting videos, podcasts, and other materials that you might find useful for staying consistent and expanding your new practice. We'll continue to provide you stories for motivation, and we'll keep sprinkling in affirmations along the way to keep your brain active in making your gratitude practice a part of your DNA.

The Daily Content

Every single piece of content you're getting is a product of countless hours of sweat and research done by our team to ensure we're doing our best to:

1. Light a fire in you to succeed in adding the habit.
2. Provide you with the necessary knowledge and information to make mastering your mornings simple and easy.
3. Make adding the habit fun and interesting.

Not only is every individual piece of content chosen amongst thousands of competing options, but as mentioned in the previous section, the order of the content has been creatively designed to get you through the struggles associated with the different stages of adding habits.

DAY 1   DAY 2   DAY 3   DAY 4   DAY 5

PRO-TIP 1   PRO-TIP 2   SUCCESS STORY   DAILY CHALLENGE 1   DAILY CHALLENGE 2

Here are the different types of content you can expect:

Pro-Tips

Pro-tips are the golden little nuggets of information you get to make implementing the habit on a day-to-day basis as simple and painless as possible. The point is to give you expert tips and hacks to get you going, and the variety and diversity of the different pro-tips will provide you with countless options for how to succeed in adding the habit.

Daily Challenges

The daily challenges you'll be receiving will be immensely important to your success in practicing gratitude.

Why?

They each help target a different area of discipline that will help you force yourself to do something you wouldn't usually do - pushing you out of your comfort zone.

By strengthening this willpower muscle inside you using small, very specific daily challenges, your self-discipline will grow more and more every single day. These daily challenges apply not just to gratitude, but to all other aspects of your life — from curbing negative habits and distractions to building other healthy habits as well.

Clips & Podcasts

There's nothing as motivating as simultaneously seeing the passion in someone's eyes, hearing the truth in someone's voice, and feeling the intensity of their struggle. Connecting with people who have sat in your shoes and crossed over to the light of a daily gratitude practice will give you clear reference points that you *can* succeed at this, just as others who have struggled have. Watching or listening to inspirational and informational content will serve as the informative reminder you need to get started and push through your normal, expected struggles.

Food For Thought

Breaking the cycle of the way we ordinarily think and creating new associations is in reality, extremely difficult. New ideas we've never thought about are extremely useful for breaking our usual associative thinking so that new thoughts can come in place of our old thoughts.

This content will provide you material that will give you an opportunity to think about things differently - the same way the journal as a whole will begin to help you perceive your life differently!

Affirmations

Affirmations and visualization are highly effective tools used by some of the most successful people to have ever lived. From athletes to actors to CEOs, affirmations are used to help channel positive energy towards goals and create an inevitable connection between your present self and the end goal you have in mind.

What Affirmations Really Do

1. Subconsciously tap into your creativity muscle to begin generating creative ways of reaching your goals.

2. Subconsciously program your brain to associate yourself with the end goal you have in mind, and prepares you to mentally sort out the steps necessary to get from where you are right now to your end goals.

3. Attract you to your goal by the simple act of envisioning yourself where you want to ultimately be.

4. Motivate you in the sense that it literally causes your brain to believe that you have within you the power, ability and capability to get exactly where you want in life.

So what does it mean to use affirmations?

Using affirmations is the act of repeating to yourself that you already are the person you want to be.

It leads you towards envisioning that you can achieve your life goals and you can be exactly the person you ideally view yourself to be.

It is the repeating of idealistic situations you would like to see yourself in, except you say them in the present tense, as if they were true now.

While repeating these affirmations, you visualize yourself as this ideal person, in the ideal situation you want to see yourself in, which trains your brain to believe it is possible.

The 'How'

Perfectionists, Tread Lightly.
The Importance of Not Getting Caught Up With Being Perfect.

Of course, we'd all love to feel happy and be positive all the time no matter what the circumstances.

In reality, it's impossible. There is no such thing as a perfectly happy life. The only way to have a perfectly happy life is to see your life as such. You're not just going to pick this journal up and be a different person.

That's why it's so important to understand that you can't FAKE this process, and you are NOT going to be perfect.

Shooting for perfection before you even start the journal can prevent you from taking even one step in the direction of your goal.

There's one simple concept that shatters all the best research, tips, and strategies you can look for (that you'll be getting through this journal anyways).

Here it is… the best way to be more grateful is…..

You realize one thing you're genuinely grateful for.

You start thinking about ONE area of your life you sincerely appreciate.

You make SOME effort to change your perception.

Don't let the desire to reach perfection - the possibility of feeling overwhelming gratitude every day - stop you from feeling grateful for just one thing today.

Don't waste your energy fantasizing and searching.

Nobody ELSE can force you to feel grateful. It'll only come by thinking about your life and understanding how blessed you are.

You'll be getting all the information and motivation you need from us on a daily basis in the form of daily content.

You won't PERSONALLY think every piece of content is useful. You won't think every tip will be effective. You won't think every podcast is insightful. You won't think every affirmation is worthwhile.

But if you make an attempt to use every piece of content, you'll see results. Pinky promise. Disregard the upside you *expect* out of it before trying it — take action first.

Every little action you take propels a snowball effect that greatly impacts other areas of your life.

Success is all about taking small, consistent actions over time.

Important: **you do not need to finish this journal in 66 consecutive calendar days in order for it to be effective!**

In fact, every single person who has ever embarked on a journey to build gratitude as a habit has days where they completely forget about it.

Instead of trying to gloss over this, we're choosing to take a more practical approach by preparing specifically for those days of failure that will most likely blindside you when you least expect it.

There's two keys to using these struggle days in a way that will benefit you:

First, empathize with yourself in situations where you realize you're taking your circumstances for granted. Don't just think about it, actually feel what you'd be experiencing (e.g. if you were very motivated and one day you slipped up). Put yourself in that headspace.

Second, write out what the most disciplined version of yourself would do in that state, post-failure. Some examples of what your most disciplined self might do:

- Remove all guilt as you realize it's useless. Instead, you immediately search for WHY this happened.

- You get genuinely excited to keep going because you realize that you love challenges - each one you surpass makes you a stronger person.

- This time, you're mentally equipped with all you need to not let this specific mistake happen again.

- You realize this is a completely normal part of the self-improvement process - you gather all your energy, recoup mentally, and attack your day regardless.

Now, for the first time you truly struggle - what would you tell yourself and what would your actions be?

_____

_____

_____

_____

_____

_____

_____

_____

You don't have to do this exactly when you face your first struggle point, but having this as a reference can be extremely useful.

Sample Content Page

Butterfly vs. Bee

When you see a butterfly flying around on a sunny day, you can't help but feel a warm opening inside of you. You welcome the butterfly emotionally, and you're usually so glad to see it. It's always a wonderful surprise that brings warmth into your experience, even if just for a moment.

When you see a bee, especially when it comes close to you, you usually close up. It's like you emotionally reject the bee because you're thrown into fight or flight mode and the only thing you want in the world is for that bee to leave you alone.

It's incredible what a drastic difference it makes in terms of what we experience when we see a bee vs. when we see a butterfly. But how many times have you really been stung by a bee? Once? Twice?

If you examine yourself a little more closely, you'll see that the only real difference is the way you perceive each of these insects. Your response is conditioned based on what you've always thought when you see or come in contact with each one.

Our perception is EVERYTHING. Next time you see a bee, try to see what happens inside of you, and see if you can prevent from closing up. Rather than close emotionally and feel fear, try to open and think of the bee as another living being. See if it changes your experience!

"Gratitude is the healthiest of all human emotions. The more you express gratitude for what you have, the more likely you will have even more to express gratitude for.." - Zig Ziglar

Sample Journal Page

 WHAT AM I GRATEFUL FOR TODAY?
(OPTIONAL THEME: RELATIONSHIPS)

1. Knowing how many people love me, inside and out
2. All of the incredible friendships I've built in my life
3. The knuckle dimples on my baby's chubby hands

 BENEFITS I FELT TODAY (CIRCLE):

Feel Happier · More Creative · Increased Confidence · Felt Lighter · More Energized · Reduced Anxiety

 IN WHAT WAYS COULD I BE WAY LESS FORTUNATE THAN I AM NOW?

I've been stressing out about all the things I'm juggling between work and home demands... but really I'm beyond lucky to even have an amazing family and rewarding job.

 HOW COULD I SHIFT MY SELF-TALK TO BE MUCH MORE SUPPORTIVE, AS IF I WERE MY OWN BEST FRIEND?

By remembering that I'm a powerful, beautiful soul who's always looking out for others and improving the world!

MINI GRATITUDE ACTION OF THE DAY:

Completed?

THINK OF SOMETHING YOU MAY DO IN THE FUTURE THAT YOU'LL BE VERY CRITICAL OF YOURSELF FOR. MAKE A PACT NOW THAT YOU'LL BE RIDICULOUSLY EMPOWERING AND SUPPORTIVE INSTEAD.

A Simple Idea

We hope that after reading the introductory pages, you're motivated and ready to tackle tomorrow morning with every ounce of energy you have.

We'll leave you to it with one simple idea.

Tomorrow, you will be exactly who you are **today**.

The rest of your life is a future projection of who you are today.

If you **change** today, tomorrow will be **different**.

If you **don't change** today, the rest of your life is **pre-determined**.

Commit.

No matter what happens tomorrow...

*whether I am exhausted
or have the **worst** day of my life...*

*...whether I win the lottery
or have the **best** day of my life...*

*I **will** work on my gratitude habit.*

*My word is like **gold.***

*I will do whatever it takes
to make this happen.*

I **will** do my morning routine this week (circle one):

(**On Weekdays Only**)   (**Every Damn Day**)

_____   _____
Signature   Date

PHASE 1:

DAYS 1-7

Phase 1	Phase 2	Phase 3
Days 01-07	Days 08-21	Days 22-66+
Hell Week.	Staying Consistent.	Rewiring Your Brain.

Phase 1: Hell Week

When beginning a new habit, what's really important is getting to the point where you start to see the benefits you expect. It isn't going to be easy to start. You need to believe in yourself and take at least one concrete step in the direction of your goal every single day during this phase because it's really easy to lose hope right off the bat.

Make use of every tip, every affirmation, and all the motivation you're getting to make it as easy as possible to take just one action towards your goal every day. Remember, we want to get to the point where we see benefits, and from that point on, self-motivation to re-acquire those benefits comes into play and smooths out the process.

Let's do this.

Day 1: **Pro-Tip**

Don't avoid the negative.

Robert Emmons, one of the leading gratitude researchers in the world, says that while we often associate gratitude with focusing on the good and avoiding the bad. The key to leading a thankful life is embracing setbacks as part of your overall journey.

Although gratitude generates positive emotion, which in turn fosters optimism and hope, our aim is to cultivate a mindset of gratitude.

We are **all** on this crazy journey.

For whatever reason, we happen to be here on this remote planet in a corner of the universe. For whatever reason, we were born into the life we happen to be living.

Ups and downs are inevitable. The journey comes with success, failure, joy, pain, happiness, sorrow, adventure, static periods, reflective periods, health, sickness… it's all a part of the journey.

For whatever reason, we find ourselves on this ride we call life. Everything we experience in our lives is just another part of the ride.

Embrace it all. Express it all. Own every inch of the good, the bad, and the ugly.

"Happiness can be found even in the darkest of times, if one only remembers to turn on the light.." - Albus Dumbledore

I am an amazing person. I have a beautiful heart. I instinctively do what's good for the world and others.

WHAT AM I GRATEFUL FOR TODAY?
(OPTIONAL THEME: RELATIONSHIPS)

1. _____

2. _____

3. _____

BENEFITS I FELT TODAY (CIRCLE):

Feel Happier	More Creative	Increased Confidence	Felt Lighter	More Energized	Reduced Anxiety

WHAT AM I TAKING FOR GRANTED IN MY LIFE?

_____

_____

_____

HOW COULD I SHIFT MY SELF-TALK TO BE MUCH MORE SUPPORTIVE, AS IF I WERE MY OWN BEST FRIEND?

_____

_____

MINI GRATITUDE ACTION OF THE DAY (OPTIONAL):

Completed?

ADD A REMINDER IN YOUR PHONE FOR LUNCHTIME TOMORROW TO FIND SOMETHING TO BE GRATEFUL FOR!

43

Day 2: **Daily Challenge**

Challenge: Change your perspective.

Perspective is everything.

The way I interpret my circumstances determines how I feel about my life, and how I feel determines how I respond to the events taking place in my life.

Try and think about a difficult circumstance you're dealing with now, or one you've dealt with recently. It could be an argument with another person, feeling sorry for yourself for some reason, a situation you can't avoid that scares you… anything.

Is there ANY way to think about the situation with an attitude in which you're actually grateful for something? Can you be grateful to have the opportunity to be in the position you're in rather than focus on what's difficult about it? Is there any way to look at the situation and see something different than you've been telling yourself about it?

The answer is yes, no matter what you're facing. If you can't come up with anything, ask another person who can really be honest with you whether they think there's another possible perspective.

☐ I completed this daily challenge.

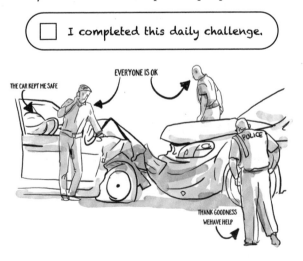

I am kind. I care deeply for my family. I know how to maintain the right boundaries for myself.

♡ WHAT AM I GRATEFUL FOR TODAY?
(OPTIONAL THEME: EVERY-DAY THINGS)

1. _____

2. _____

3. _____

✓ BENEFITS I FELT TODAY (CIRCLE):

☺					
Feel Happier	More Creative	Increased Confidence	Felt Lighter	More Energized	Reduced Anxiety

👀 IN WHAT WAYS COULD I BE WAY LESS FORTUNATE THAN I AM NOW?

_____

_____

_____

♡ WHAT'S SOMETHING I DID THAT I STILL REGRET? HOW CAN I EMPATHIZE WITH MYSELF FOR IT AND LEARN FROM IT INSTEAD?

_____

_____

🔥 MINI GRATITUDE ACTION OF THE DAY:

Completed?

TEXT A LOVED ONE ABOUT SOMETHING THEY DID THAT SHOWED A LOT ABOUT THEIR CHARACTER AND HOW YOU APPRECIATE THEM FOR IT.

☐

Day 3: **Pro-Tip**

Don't be picky!

When we begin to try and make a practice of gratitude, it's easy to start with the big things. Family, friends, other relationships are the go-to for most people, and that's all fantastic.

But in order to make a habit of gratitude, we have to open our eyes much bigger than the first thing that comes to mind. Right now, I'm typing this on a laptop I had the money to buy, to do work that I love to do. The laptop is on this genius anti-gravity invention called a table that someone invented thousands of years ago, and I'm drinking a cup of warm tea that I get to enjoy.

The habit of being grateful starts with appreciating every good thing in life and recognizing there's nothing too small to be grateful for.

Something as small as appreciating wonderful weather, getting a package you've been waiting for, appreciating the fact that you have unlimited access to clean running water, or even that you have somewhere to sleep at night.

Our blessings are literally limitless. If we can slowly begin to open our eyes and think more often about how lucky we are, our lives will change drastically, simply by the act of changing how we perceive things.

"Whenever you are about to find fault with someone, ask yourself the following question: What fault of mine most nearly resembles the one I am about to criticize?" - Marcus Aurelius

I make an impact in the world, even if it's only sharing a smile with a stranger. I am stronger than the negative thoughts and emotions of others, of myself.

DATE _____

WHAT AM I GRATEFUL FOR TODAY?
(OPTIONAL THEME: MY BODY)

1. _____

2. _____

3. _____

BENEFITS I FELT TODAY (CIRCLE):

Feel Happier   More Creative   Increased Confidence   Felt Lighter   More Energized   Reduced Anxiety

KNOWING WHAT I KNOW TODAY, HOW WOULD I GUIDE MY YOUNGER SELF THROUGH A DIFFICULT SITUATION I WENT THROUGH?

_____

_____

_____

HOW COULD I BE MORE SUPPORTIVE OF MYSELF?

_____

_____

MINI GRATITUDE ACTION OF THE DAY:

Completed?

IF YOU COME ACROSS ANY WORKING PERSON YOU SEE ON A REGULAR BASIS (I.E. YOUR BARISTA AT A COFFEE SHOP), LET THEM KNOW HOW MUCH YOU APPRECIATE THE SERVICE THEY PROVIDE.

47

Day 4: **Daily Challenge**

Challenge: Write a gratitude letter.

There are very few things that can make us feel as grateful as sitting down, spending time writing a heartfelt letter, and delivering it to the person we wrote it for. The process of writing on its own fosters an incredibly strong sense of appreciation, and the response from the person it is given to exponentially enhances how good it feels.

Write a gratitude letter today and see how it impacts you. If you do this challenge, you will LOVE it. Writing gratitude letters is also something you can do regularly - it never gets old.

1. Choose someone you feel really lucky to have in your life, or someone who did something for you that you would like to express your appreciation for.
2. Sit down with a pen and piece of paper and write them a letter explaining very specifically why you appreciate them so much. Let them know how they make you feel. Tell them how they've impacted your life, and what it is about them that has affected you so strongly.
3. Deliver the letter. If you have the opportunity and strength, deliver it in person.

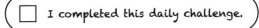

☐ I completed this daily challenge.

I have the capacity to forgive. I forgive those who have done me wrong. I am free of past wrongdoings because I choose to be.

WHAT AM I GRATEFUL FOR TODAY?
(OPTIONAL THEME: COINCIDENCES)

1. _____

2. _____

3. _____

BENEFITS I FELT TODAY (CIRCLE):

Feel Happier	More Creative	Increased Confidence	Felt Lighter	More Energized	Reduced Anxiety

HOW DO I UTILIZE MY TALENTS AND ABILITIES IN WAYS I DON'T THINK ABOUT OR FULLY APPRECIATE?

_____

_____

_____

WHAT CAN I FORGIVE MYSELF FOR?

_____

_____

MINI GRATITUDE ACTION OF THE DAY:

Completed?

LEAVE A REVIEW FOR A BUSINESS (ON AMAZON, YELP, ETC.) TO THANK THEM AND THEIR STAFF FOR A RECENT EXPERIENCE YOU HAD THERE.

49

Day 5: **Daily Challenge**

**Challenge: Pay attention to the little ways you negatively respond to life.**

Newsflash: **Your responses to life are 100 times more important than you think.** Every choice you make today is building up a habit for the rest of your life. Our brains learn from what we do repeatedly.

From little things, like getting upset when someone cuts you off on the street— to big things like the way you respond to criticism from a family member, shapes who you are now and who you will become.

You can justify your own negativity, but every time you do, you're making a decision about who you are. Creating justifications is a mental habit that can absolutely be rewired. Your brain only knows **how you respond**. *All mini-decisions build up to your habits.* **You** *are* **your mini-decisions.**

☐ I completed this daily challenge.

"Empathy begins with understanding life from another person's perspective. Nobody has an objective experience of reality. It's all through our own individual prisms.." - Sterling K. Brown

I am the architect of my life. I create the world I want around me. If something isn't working, I have the power to fix it.

DATE _____

WHAT AM I GRATEFUL FOR TODAY?
(OPTIONAL THEME: WORK-RELATED)

1. _____

2. _____

3. _____

BENEFITS I FELT TODAY (CIRCLE):

Feel Happier	More Creative	Increased Confidence	Felt Lighter	More Energized	Reduced Anxiety

 ### WHAT AM I HOLDING ONTO FROM MY PAST THAT IS HOLDING ME BACK?

_____

_____

_____

IN WHAT WAYS DOES THINKING ABOUT THE PAST STOP ME FROM IMPROVING IN THE FUTURE?

_____

_____

 ### MINI GRATITUDE ACTION OF THE DAY:

Completed?

CONSIDER ONE OF YOUR BIGGEST STRENGTHS. SPEND TWO MINUTES IN GRATITUDE FOR THE EXPERIENCE/PEOPLE THAT HELPED YOU FOSTER THOSE STRENGTHS (THIS CAN BE A HARD THING, PUSH THROUGH IT.)

☐

Day 6: **Pro-Tip**

How to cool a hot temper.

One of the best ways to lessen the fury we feel when it feels like we're about to spiral out of control is to immediately change the focus of our attention from whatever is stimulating our aggression and placing it on what's good.

The next time you're about to lash out at someone or vent about how horrible things are in your life, try taking one whole minute to do a quick inventory of 3 things you're thankful for in that moment.

Don't just think of something and immediately discard it. Tell yourself what you're grateful for AND why for each thing on your list.

Immediately after, try to talk yourself down by reminding yourself that feeling angry about something never helps you deal with it… ever.

Remember: It is impossible to feel a negative emotion like anger, stress, or fear, at the same time that you are FEELING the emotion of gratitude.

"Self-awareness gives you the capacity to learn from your mistakes as well as your successes. It enables you to keep growing."
- Lawrence Bossidy

I can conquer a limitless number of challenges.
In the face of difficult moments, I have proven _____
to myself that I will get through it!   DATE

♡ WHAT AM I GRATEFUL FOR TODAY?
(OPTIONAL THEME: NATURE)

1. _____

2. _____

3. _____

✓ BENEFITS I FELT TODAY (CIRCLE):

☺	🧠	🦸	🎈	🖤	🧘
Feel Happier	More Creative	Increased Confidence	Felt Lighter	More Energized	Reduced Anxiety

DOES REACTING NEGATIVELY EVER HELP A SITUATION I HAVE NO CHOICE BUT TO DEAL WITH? HOW CAN I SHIFT MY VIEW ON THINGS INSTEAD?

_____

_____

_____

HOW DOES MY MIND EXAGGERATE THE NEGATIVE WAYS I VIEW MYSELF?

_____

_____

MINI GRATITUDE ACTION OF THE DAY:

Completed?

FIND CONTACT INFORMATION FOR A TEACHER OR PROFESSOR THAT MADE A DIFFERENCE IN YOUR LIFE AND LET THEM KNOW HOW THEY'VE AFFECTED YOU.

☐

53

Day 7: **Affirmations**

1. Find a quiet area where you can do this in private so you can be at ease. If you can't find a private space, say this in your head while pretending you're screaming it from a mountaintop.

2. Think of a time when you felt absolutely powerful - **when you felt on top of the world.** Tap into every emotion you had at that moment and get yourself into that state right now. How were you feeling then - Powerful? Unstoppable? Strong? Incredible!? Get into it now!!!!

3. Now feel your intensity grow tenfold! Say this with deep passion:

I am learning to be grateful for what I have while being excited for what is yet to come. I choose to focus on what I have rather than what I believe I lack. I choose an attitude of abundance over an attitude of scarcity.

I LOVE my gift of life!

Repeat this **one more time.**

"Gratitude is a powerful catalyst for happiness. It's the spark that lights a fire of joy in your soul." - Amy Collette

Everything that has lead to this moment has happened... not 'for a reason,' but it has happened. And I have weathered each up and down because I am incredible.

WHAT AM I GRATEFUL FOR TODAY?
(OPTIONAL THEME: OPPORTUNITIES)

1. _____

2. _____

3. _____

✓ BENEFITS I FELT TODAY (CIRCLE):

☺				⚡	
Feel Happier	More Creative	Increased Confidence	Felt Lighter	More Energized	Reduced Anxiety

WHAT BIG LIFE EVENT OR GOAL IS MY HAPPINESS ATTACHED TO?

_____

_____

_____

HOW CAN I TAKE MORE RESPONSIBILITY FOR MY OWN EMOTIONS AND BLAME OTHER PEOPLE OR EXTERNAL CIRCUMSTANCES LESS?

_____

_____

MINI GRATITUDE ACTION OF THE DAY:

Completed?

SEND FLOWERS TO A FAMILY MEMBER OR FRIEND, JUST BECAUSE.

☐

~~PHASE 1:~~

CONQUERED

Phase 1 Recap: Days 1-7

1. How successful was I in trying to apply the first week of content? What content do I want to continue to keep in mind as I move forward with this habit?

_____

_____

2. What happens to me emotionally when I change my perspective on something from negative to positive?

_____

_____

3. Does my behavior change when I'm in a grateful state? How?

_____

_____

4. What surprising things did I find myself grateful for?

_____

_____

5. Can I see how gratitude can change my life if I keep at this?

_____

_____

_____

PHASE 2:

DAYS 8-21

Phase 1 | **Phase 2** | Phase 3

Days 01-07
Hell Week.

Days 08-21
Staying Consistent.

Days 22-66+
Rewiring Your Brain.

58

Phase 2: Digging Deep - Staying Consistent

Congratulations, you've gotten through Phase 1 (Hell Week).

If you don't feel like you've made as much progress as you'd like, don't worry. One day and one victory at a time is the key.

Phase 2 is important because this is the point where we either feel like we've got it down, OR we feel hopeless that we'll never find any sense of consistency.

If you feel hopeless, you won't feel hopeless forever, as long as you continue to believe in yourself and make a real effort daily.

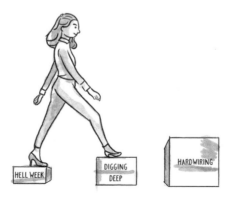

Commit.

*I KNOW this next phase
is going to be extremely hard.*

*I understand I may not
be perfect about it every day.*

*But each day, I **will** put my heart into
conquering this life-changing goal.*

**If I miss a day,
I will pick back up.**

*Off days and missed days
will NEVER stop me.*

*In the long-run,
I will win.*

---

*I **will** complete Phase 2 of this journal.*

Signature   Date

Day 8: **Daily Challenge**

Challenge: Do this 5-minute gratitude exercise.

Tony Robbins has a beautiful gratitude exercise that has never failed to spark someone in a place of true appreciation for their life. You can find it here: https://habitnest.link/tonygratitude

An abridged description of it is below:

1. Sit up with your back straight and put both hands on your heart (one on top of the other).
2. Close your eyes and breathe deeply into your heart. Take in as much air as you can and exhale it back into your own heart with as much love as possible.
3. As you continue this pattern of greeting for two minutes, keep in mind that your heart hasn't stopped beating since it was formed in your mother's womb. You didn't have to do anything to get your heart… it was given to you. And it perpetually beats for you, giving you the gift of life over and over, asking nothing from you in return.

We definitely recommend listening to the audio in full, which you can do here: https://habitnest.link/tonygratitude

☐ I completed this daily challenge.

"Empathy is seeing with the eyes of another, listening with the ears of another, and feeling with the heart of another." - Anonymous

I am a useful person. I have a heart for others' troubles and an ear for listening. I can positively impact myself and others.

WHAT AM I GRATEFUL FOR TODAY?
(OPTIONAL THEME: MY OWN TALENTS & ABILITIES)

1. _____
2. _____
3. _____

WHAT MESSAGE DO I NEED TO REMIND MYSELF OF TODAY?

_____

_____

_____

IN WHAT WAYS DO MY PRECONCEIVED IDEAS OF WHO PEOPLE ARE AFFECT MY RELATIONSHIPS?

_____

_____

_____

HOW CAN I REMOVE GUILT FROM MY LIFE?

_____

_____

MINI GRATITUDE ACTION OF THE DAY:

Completed?

SAY "THANK YOU" TO EVERYONE WHO DOES *ANYTHING* FOR YOU TODAY, EVEN IF THEY ARE "SUPPOSED" TO DO IT.

63

Day 9: **Super Read**

Title: *Thanks*

Author: Robbert Emmons

You've already seen the name Robert Emmons in this journal - that's because he's actually the world's leading scientific expert on gratitude. He's the author of close to 200 publications in peer-reviewed journals and he's written five books, all about gratitude.

His book *Thanks* is an in depth, easy-to-read guide explaining the latest research on gratitude and how the practice of gratitude can directly impact your happiness and quality of life.

Robert believes that gratitude is one of the few things that can measurably change peoples' lives.

If you'd like to understand more about the science behind gratitude and how to enhance your practice as much as possible, definitely check it out!

"Self awareness is the ability to take an honest look at your life without any attachment to it being right or wrong. good or bad." - Debbie Ford

I am at the beginning of my life, no matter my age. I have the power to make my time on Earth as wonderful as I want it to be, by changing my perceptions and expectations.

WHAT AM I GRATEFUL FOR TODAY?
(OPTIONAL THEME: EXPERIENCES)

1. _____

2. _____

3. _____

WHAT MESSAGE DO I NEED TO REMIND MYSELF OF TODAY?

_____

_____

_____

WHAT EXPERIENCE AM I GRATEFUL FOR, BUT AM GLAD IT IS OVER?

_____

_____

_____

WHY DO I JUDGE MYSELF SO HARSHLY?

_____

_____

MINI GRATITUDE ACTION OF THE DAY:

Completed?

TODAY, VIEW YOUR WORLD THROUGH A TOURIST'S EYES. HOW AMAZING ARE THE THINGS THAT YOU SEE THAT YOU MAY HAVE BECOME BLIND TO?

☐

Day 10: **Pro-Tip**

<u>*Stop comparing yourself with others.*</u>

"No one can make you feel inferior without your consent."
- Eleanor Roosevelt

Comparing ourselves to others is such a seemingly natural thing we all do. Especially now that we have so much access into other people's lives with reality TV and social media, evaluating other people's quality of life and comparing it to our own is constantly taking place for each of us - most of the time, we're not even aware we're doing it.

It is imperative that we remember that each of us primarily shares and presents only the best parts of our lives with others. We hide the pain for fear of judgment, and we care more about what our life looks like to other people, rather than what it's actually like.

We're harmed both by thinking that other people have better lives than us, and by trying to make it look like our life is better than other peoples'. ***What does it actually matter what someone else's life is like?***

My life is mine to be lived and experienced. Comparing myself to other people in a way that makes me feel bad about myself has absolutely no benefit whatsoever.

I refuse to sweat the small stuff. This thing that is causing me discomfort will not mean anything in a year... maybe not even in a month.

WHAT AM I GRATEFUL FOR TODAY?
(OPTIONAL THEME: TECHNOLOGY)

1. _____

2. _____

3. _____

WHAT MESSAGE DO I NEED TO REMIND MYSELF OF TODAY?

_____

_____

_____

WHAT WAS THE LAST NICE THING I DID FOR SOMEBODY?

_____

_____

_____

WHAT 'WRONG' CAN I 'RIGHT' WITH THE HELP OF GRATITUDE?

_____

_____

MINI GRATITUDE ACTION OF THE DAY:

Completed?

IF YOU HAVE A FAMILY, MAKE IT A POINT TO ASK EACH MEMBER WHAT THEY'RE GRATEFUL FOR TODAY. IF YOU DON'T, ASK YOUR FRIENDS!

Day 11: **Affirmations**

1. Find a quiet area where you can do this in private so you can be at ease. If you can't find a private space, say this in your head while pretending you're screaming it from a mountaintop.

2. Think of a time when you felt absolutely powerful - **when you felt on top of the world.** Tap into every emotion you had at that moment and get yourself into that state right now. How were you feeling then - Powerful? Unstoppable? Strong? Incredible!? Get into it now!!!!

3. Now feel your intensity grow tenfold! Say this with deep passion:

I see that each moment presents me a unique opportunity to spread what I'm feeling, and I choose to spread positivity love, joy, and gratefulness. When I spread positive emotions, they are always reciprocated. My own joy grows stronger and bigger.

Repeat this **one more time.**

"True empathy requires that you step outside your own emotions to view things entirely from the perspective of the other person." - Anonymous

I am incomparable. There is no one like me. For this reason, I will not try to compare myself to others or judge others. They are incomparable, too.

WHAT AM I GRATEFUL FOR TODAY?
(OPTIONAL THEME: ADVERSITY)

1. _____

2. _____

3. _____

WHAT MESSAGE DO I NEED TO REMIND MYSELF OF TODAY?

_____

_____

_____

HOW CAN I CHANGE MY MINDSET TO ATTRACT THE LIFE I TRULY WANT?

_____

_____

_____

IF I LOOKED AT MYSELF FROM THE PERSPECTIVE OF A CAREGIVER, HOW WOULD I GUIDE MYSELF TO HAPPINESS?

_____

_____

MINI GRATITUDE ACTION OF THE DAY:

Completed?

SEND AN EMAIL TO THE AUTHOR OF YOUR FAVORITE BOOK (OR LEAVE A BOOK REVIEW) AND TELL THEM WHY YOU LOVED THE BOOK SO MUCH.

Day 12: **Food For Thought**

_28,835_

The average life expectancy in the United States is 79 years old. The number 1 ranked country in terms of life expectancy is Japan with the average being 84 years. All other countries fall in between a range of 50-84.

So in the United States, the average number of days lived is 28,835.

We don't usually think about our own mortality unless we get sick, someone close to us gets sick, or other people we know pass away.

Once in a while, it's important to think about the fact that we're not going to live forever because it helps put things into perspective and gives us a chance to think about what's important.

Ask yourself:

Based on the way I live, what does it seem like I value most?

Does the way I live reflect what I truly believe is important in life?

Do I appreciate this opportunity of life enough to live a life based on what I value?

"You can't get away from yourself by moving from one place to another."
- Ernest Hemingway

I refuse to quit. I know that there are many possible solutions to any given problem and I WILL figure this out.

DATE _____

WHAT AM I GRATEFUL FOR TODAY?
(OPTIONAL THEME: RELATIONSHIPS)

1. _____

2. _____

3. _____

WHAT MESSAGE DO I NEED TO REMIND MYSELF OF TODAY?

_____

_____

_____

IN WHAT WAYS COULD I BE WAY LESS FORTUNATE THAN I AM NOW?

_____

_____

_____

HOW COULD I SHIFT MY SELF-TALK TO BE MUCH MORE SUPPORTIVE, AS IF I WERE MY OWN BEST FRIEND?

_____

_____

 MINI GRATITUDE ACTION OF THE DAY:

Completed?

SEND A CARE PACKAGE TO A MEMBER OF THE MILITARY SERVING OVERSEAS:
https://supportourtroops.org/care-packages

☐

Day 13: **Pro-Tip**

It could always be harder.

Although it's always better to focus on yourself without considering others, when you're struggling to find a feeling of gratitude and appreciation, it can be helpful to put yourself in the shoes of someone who is experiencing misfortunes greater than your own.

Putting yourself in the shoes of other people who have endured difficulties like debilitating physical, financial, emotional, or mental conditions can help us see how fortunate we are.

This is particularly helpful when you find yourself in a state of self-pity. When you find yourself complaining about a situation you have to deal with or something else you're experiencing that's hard, remembering how much worse things can be is a very useful tool.

We take everything for granted. Remember that when you find yourself complaining!

"In ordinary life, we hardly realize that we receive a great deal more than we give, and that it is only with gratitude that life becomes rich."
- Dietrich Bonhoeffer

I have the courage to say "no." Agreeing to commitments or statements that aren't true to myself doesn't make me a better person. I will be protective of my time and my energy.

WHAT AM I GRATEFUL FOR TODAY?
(OPTIONAL THEME: EVERY-DAY THINGS)

1. _____
2. _____
3. _____

WHAT MESSAGE DO I NEED TO REMIND MYSELF OF TODAY?

_____

_____

_____

WHAT AM I TAKING FOR GRANTED IN MY LIFE?

_____

_____

_____

WHAT'S SOMETHING I DID THAT I STILL REGRET? HOW CAN I EMPATHIZE WITH MYSELF FOR IT AND LEARN FROM IT INSTEAD?

_____

_____

MINI GRATITUDE ACTION OF THE DAY:

Completed?

WRITE A SELF-SUPPORT NOTE OR GRATITUDE QUOTE FOR YOURSELF ON YOUR BATHROOM MIRROR AND KEEP IT THERE FOR A WEEK. (WHITEBOARD MARKERS WORK GREAT FOR THIS.)

Day 14: **Favorite Podcasts**

The Science of Happiness podcast

The Science of Happiness is all about research-tested strategies for a happier, more meaningful life. It draws on the science of compassion, gratitude, mindfulness, and awe.

It is hosted by award-winning professor Dacher Keltner, and it's co-produced by PRI and UC Berkeley's Greater Good Science Center.

The podcast is really about the more important things in life - our experience of it.

An episode you might want to check out is Episode 7: *How Gratitude Benefits Your Brain.*

"We think we listen, but very rarely do we listen with real understanding, true empathy. Yet listening, of this very special kind, is one of the most potent forces for change that I know." - Carl Rogers

*I choose faith over fear. Fear will only hold
me back. Faith will power me forward.*

WHAT AM I GRATEFUL FOR TODAY?
(OPTIONAL THEME: MY BODY)

1. _____

2. _____

3. _____

WHAT MESSAGE DO I NEED TO REMIND MYSELF OF TODAY?

_____

_____

_____

KNOWING WHAT I KNOW TODAY, HOW WOULD I GUIDE MY YOUNGER SELF THROUGH A DIFFICULT SITUATION I WENT THROUGH?

_____

_____

_____

HOW COULD I BE MORE SUPPORTIVE OF MYSELF?

_____

_____

MINI GRATITUDE ACTION OF THE DAY:

Completed?

CALL SOMEONE YOU HAVEN'T BEEN ABLE TO GIVE AS MUCH ATTENTION TO
RECENTLY AND LET THEM KNOW YOU'RE THINKING OF THEM.

Day 15: **Daily Challenge**

**Challenge: 'Pay it forward' to someone today with no expectation of anything in return.**

You've probably heard of the 'pay it forward' challenge before. The idea is that you do something nice for another person simply to do something nice for another person. Your action will in turn create happiness and joy in another, which will carry on into that person's actions.

When we hear things often, we become desensitized to them, but this is an extremely powerful challenge because it has an actual impact in the world in ways we will never see. The way we feel in any given moment determines our actions. When we're upset about something, it shows in our face, our physical posture, and in the way we act. When we're feeling good, we're much more likely to take things lightly, to respond rationally, to be kind.

The best part is that when we do something nice for someone else - it makes us feel really, really good.

Here are some examples of things you can do to pay it forward:

1. Pay for a random person's cup of coffee or meal
2. Give someone an honest compliment
3. Listen to a random person's story
4. Be patient with people who provide customer service
5. Send a nice email, text, or note to someone you know
6. Donate things you don't need
7. Smile at people who walk by you

☐ I completed this daily challenge.

I choose not to take things personally. Not every statement is a personal attack. Not everything is about me.

WHAT AM I GRATEFUL FOR TODAY?
(OPTIONAL THEME: COINCIDENCES)

1. _____

2. _____

3. _____

WHAT MESSAGE DO I NEED TO REMIND MYSELF OF TODAY?

_____

_____

_____

HOW DO I UTILIZE MY TALENTS AND ABILITIES IN WAYS I DON'T THINK ABOUT OR FULLY APPRECIATE?

_____

_____

_____

WHAT CAN I FORGIVE MYSELF FOR?

_____

_____

MINI GRATITUDE ACTION OF THE DAY:

Completed?

☐

SPEND TIME IN NATURE TODAY. EVEN IF IT IS A 5-MINUTE WALK IN A BUSY NEIGHBORHOOD, LOOK FOR EVERYTHING NATURAL AND APPRECIATE IT!

Day 16: **Affirmations**

1. Find a quiet area where you can do this in private so you can be at ease. If you can't find a private space, say this in your head while pretending you're screaming it from a mountaintop.

2. Think of a time when you felt absolutely powerful - **when you felt on top of the world.** Tap into every emotion you had at that moment and get yourself into that state right now. How were you feeling then - Powerful? Unstoppable? Strong? Incredible!? Get into it now!!!!

3. Now feel your intensity grow tenfold! Say this with deep passion:

I am grateful for the opportunity to act on my desires and goals. I understand that when I appreciate the opportunity rather than resent the steps I have to take, I am much more likely to take positive action in the right direction.

Repeat this **one more time.**

"Be thankful for what you have; you'll end up having more. If you concentrate on what you don't have, you will never, ever have enough."
- Oprah Winfrey

My body is incredible. It works on its own, without my effort. I will pay attention to how much I appreciate this vessel that is bringing me through the world.

WHAT AM I GRATEFUL FOR TODAY?
(OPTIONAL THEME: WORK-RELATED)

1. _____

2. _____

3. _____

WHAT MESSAGE DO I NEED TO REMIND MYSELF OF TODAY?

_____

_____

_____

WHAT AM I HOLDING ONTO FROM MY PAST THAT IS HOLDING ME BACK?

_____

_____

_____

IN WHAT WAYS DOES THINKING ABOUT THE PAST STOP ME FROM IMPROVING IN THE FUTURE?

_____

_____

MINI GRATITUDE ACTION OF THE DAY:

Completed?

THE NEXT TIME YOU ARE IN A SOCIAL SITUATION, START THE CONVERSATION POSITIVELY AND STEER IT AWAY FROM COMPLAINING AND GOSSIP.

Day 17: **Pro-Tip**

Savor the good times.

We're always chasing good times. We chase happiness in the way we live, no matter how we live our lives.

But for some reason, when those moments show up, the ones in which we find ourselves happy, doing something fun, spending time with people we care about… we forget to really be in that moment and enjoy it because we're too busy focusing on other parts of our lives.

So today's pro-tip is about _**savoring the good moments**_. If you notice you're feeling happy, no matter what it is you're doing, stop for a moment and bring your attention to what's actually happening in that moment. Just stop and take in everything about the moment.

Notice how you feel, including the sensations in your body and the thoughts you're having. Take in what's happening both inside of you and around you outside. Later, when you're trying to find gratitude, you can remember this moment and experience the benefits all over again.

"Empathy is simply listening, holding space, withholding judgment, emotionally connecting, and communicating that incredibly healing message of you're not alone." - Brene Brown

I deserve love and friendship. I give my heart without expecting anything in return. I am loved more than I know.

WHAT AM I GRATEFUL FOR TODAY?
(OPTIONAL THEME: NATURE)

1. _____
2. _____
3. _____

WHAT MESSAGE DO I NEED TO REMIND MYSELF OF TODAY?

_____

_____

_____

DOES REACTING NEGATIVELY EVER HELP A SITUATION I HAVE NO CHOICE BUT TO DEAL WITH? HOW CAN I SHIFT MY VIEW ON THINGS INSTEAD?

_____

_____

_____

HOW DOES MY MIND EXAGGERATE THE NEGATIVE WAYS I VIEW MYSELF?

_____

_____

MINI GRATITUDE ACTION OF THE DAY:

Completed?

TODAY, THINK ABOUT A SITUATION/TIME WHEN THINGS WENT BADLY. WHAT WENT WELL? WHAT POSITIVE CAME OUT OF THE BAD WHICH YOU MAY NOT HAVE SEEN AT THE TIME?

81

Day 18: **Recommended Podcasts** 🎙️

<u>The Positive Psychology Podcast</u>

The Positive Psychology Podcast is hosted by Kristen Truempy. This is another podcast about the science of a good life.

Kristen takes a more practical approach to positive thinking and explores the science behind long term satisfaction with life: accepting and coping with 'what is' and developing skills to make the best of any situation.

Kristen wanted to provide the average person a way to understand the science that positive psychology practitioners are exploring, in a way that doesn't come in the format of a scientific paper. And she has done a great job making it fun.

We recommend checking out Episode 95, which is all about understanding how to differentiate between emotions and why it's helpful to do so.

You can find it by searching for *The Positive Psychology Podcast* on any podcast outlet.

"I think self-awareness is probably the most important thing towards being a champion." - Billie Jean King

My negative thoughts are disappearing every day, because I am mindful of their effect on my wellbeing. I am working hard at appreciating instead of judging.

WHAT AM I GRATEFUL FOR TODAY?
(OPTIONAL THEME: OPPORTUNITIES)

1. _____

2. _____

3. _____

WHAT MESSAGE DO I NEED TO REMIND MYSELF OF TODAY?

_____

_____

_____

WHAT BIG LIFE EVENT OR GOAL IS MY HAPPINESS ATTACHED TO?

_____

_____

_____

HOW CAN I TAKE MORE RESPONSIBILITY FOR MY OWN EMOTIONS AND BLAME OTHER PEOPLE OR EXTERNAL CIRCUMSTANCES LESS?

_____

_____

MINI GRATITUDE ACTION OF THE DAY:

Completed?

WRITE DOWN YOUR FAVORITE MEMORY WITH A CLOSE FRIEND. EXPLAIN IN DETAIL WHY THIS MEMORY IS SO AWESOME. SEND IT TO THEM AFTERWARDS.

□

Day 19: **Pro-Tip**

Spend time alone!

These days, we spend so little time by ourselves without doing anything. Our phones, computers, pads, and TVs consume our attention in ways we really aren't aware of. It's almost like alone time = phone time.

But being able to spend time alone, especially without the use of electronics, is not only extremely refreshing, but can improve our self-esteem. Spending time with yourself, without being distracted, can feel really good. You can literally do anything - cook, clean, garden, have a meal, sit quietly, read a book… anything. But do it alone, and without being distracted by notifications on your phone or other electronics!

It helps bring you to the moment rather than constantly being taken out of the moment with the non-stop digital content we're always consuming these days. Our attention is usually so consumed we don't even have a chance to think about being grateful for any given moment.

So spend some time alone without distractions, and see if you can find a way to bring gratitude into your attention.

"No one who achieves success does so without the help of others. The wise and confident acknowledge this help with gratitude."
- Alfred North Whitehead

I don't just love... I LIKE myself. I enjoy being who I am and spending time with the person I have become through the years. I am my own best friend.

WHAT AM I GRATEFUL FOR TODAY?
(OPTIONAL THEME: MY OWN TALENTS & ABILITIES)

1. _____

2. _____

3. _____

WHAT MESSAGE DO I NEED TO REMIND MYSELF OF TODAY?

_____

_____

_____

IN WHAT WAYS DO MY PRECONCEIVED IDEAS OF WHO PEOPLE ARE AFFECT MY RELATIONSHIPS?

_____

_____

_____

HOW CAN I REMOVE GUILT FROM MY LIFE?

_____

_____

MINI GRATITUDE ACTION OF THE DAY:

Completed?

DONATE ANY AMOUNT OF MONEY TO A CAUSE YOU SUPPORT.

☐

Day 20: **Affirmations**

1. Find a quiet area where you can do this in private so you can be at ease. If you can't find a private space, say this in your head while pretending you're screaming it from a mountaintop.

2. Think of a time when you felt absolutely powerful - **when you felt on top of the world**. Tap into every emotion you had at that moment and get yourself into that state right now. How were you feeling then - Powerful? Unstoppable? Strong? Incredible!? Get into it now!!!!

3. Now feel your intensity grow tenfold! Say this with deep passion:

I have a roof over my head. I have food on my table. The rest is up to me and how I choose to perceive things. The effect that every situation has on me is dependent on my perspective. I wish to see goodness and to spread goodness. I am beginning to understand that how I perceive determines how I act.

Repeat this **one more time.**

"Empathy is the ability to step outside of your own bubble and into the bubbles of other people." - C. Joybell

I will stop apologizing so much, especially apologizing for being myself. I am allowed to be who I am and make no concessions for this.

WHAT AM I GRATEFUL FOR TODAY?
(OPTIONAL THEME: EXPERIENCES)

1. _____

2. _____

3. _____

WHAT MESSAGE DO I NEED TO REMIND MYSELF OF TODAY?

_____

_____

_____

WHAT EXPERIENCE AM I GRATEFUL FOR, BUT AM GLAD IT IS OVER?

_____

_____

_____

WHY DO I JUDGE MYSELF SO HARSHLY?

_____

_____

MINI GRATITUDE ACTION OF THE DAY:

Completed?

SPEND TIME WITH (OR AT LEAST CALL) SOMEONE YOU KNOW ADMIRES YOU. FIND GRATITUDE FOR THEIR RESPECT.

Day 21: **Food For Thought**

Nothing valuable ever comes easy.

Have you ever thought about the fact that the most valuable things in life require the most work? The more valuable a given thing is, the harder you have to work to get it.

At the same time, we only work for what we truly value. If you're not working hard for something, rest assured that you don't value that thing as much as you think you do!

It is EXTREMELY hard to change our mindset from how we usually perceive events, to looking at things with a grateful disposition. Becoming aware of it is only the first hurdle to jump over, followed by intentionally changing the way you contextualize how you view things to be through a lens of gratitude.

But, the fact that it is so difficult is like a sign telling you how valuable it is. Understanding this helps you appreciate the process of things. Appreciate the process that opportunities present, along with the adversity they come with. Because nothing valuable ever comes easy.

"In the light of calm and steady self-awareness, inner energies wake up and work miracles without any effort on your part."
- Nisargadatta Maharaj

I am grateful that I am able to read. If all else in the world falls apart, I will always have the ability to escape into a good book.

WHAT AM I GRATEFUL FOR TODAY?
(OPTIONAL THEME: TECHNOLOGY)

1. _____

2. _____

3. _____

WHAT MESSAGE DO I NEED TO REMIND MYSELF OF TODAY?

_____

_____

_____

WHAT WAS THE LAST NICE THING I DID FOR SOMEBODY?

_____

_____

_____

WHAT 'WRONG' CAN I 'RIGHT' WITH THE HELP OF GRATITUDE?

_____

_____

 ### MINI GRATITUDE ACTION OF THE DAY:

Completed?

TELL SOMEONE YOU KNOW IS GOING THROUGH A DIFFICULT TIME THAT YOU'RE THERE FOR THEM AND GIVE THEM YOUR UNDIVIDED ATTENTION.

☐

~~PHASE 2:~~

DESTROYED.

Phase 2 Recap: Days 8-21

1.What content from Phase 2 do I want to keep working with?

_____

_____

2. What have I learned about myself during Phase 2?

_____

_____

3. How is my gratitude practice affecting my life?

_____

_____

4. How would I define gratitude now after practicing it for two weeks?

_____

_____

_____

5. In which areas of my life is my gratitude practice lacking most?

_____

_____

_____

PHASE 3:

DAYS 22-66+

 ~~Phase 1~~    ~~Phase 2~~   **Phase 3**

~~Days 01-07~~   ~~Days 08-21~~   **Days 22-66+**
~~Hell Week.~~   ~~Staying Consistent.~~ **Rewiring Your Brain.**

Phase 3: Hardwiring - Retaining Interest In Your Personal Improvement

Congratulations, you've made it to Phase 3. You've shown serious commitment to the incredible future you envision for yourself.

This is a great phase to explore how to make the most out of this habit for you, personally. Most people use this phase to experiment with different routines, wakeup times, hours of sleep, etc. to tweak what works for them.

It's easy to take the benefits you're feeling for granted — it's extremely easy to fall off the wagon, especially in this phase.

Keep going strong until being a productive early riser is engrained in your DNA.

This means pushing through to stick with your commitments on your best days, your worst days, and especially the days where you just don't feel like it (those are the *most important*).

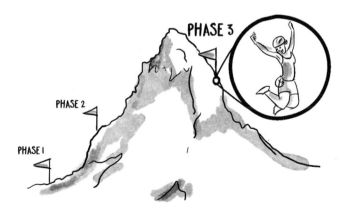

Commit.

I am INCREDIBLE.

I've come a long way,
but the road doesn't end here.

It's time to ingrain this habit in me forever.

I will see this
huge challenge all the way through.

Mastering this habit is only the
beginning of my perpetual growth.

Nothing will stop me now.

Signature

Date

Phase 2 Medal
Earned!

Day 22: **Pro-Tip**

<u>Spend more time in nature.</u>

There are very few things that really bring us to the sense of awe that comes with realizing that we're alive in this beautiful world like spending time in nature.

Getting out and simply observing the trees, looking at the sky, feeling the wind, experiencing the most natural conditions of life invites a sense of wonder and magic. With that sense of wonder comes a deep appreciation for the magnificent way things are on this planet.

There are so many ways to come in contact with the nature around us. You could walk on the beach, go on a hike, walk around in an area with a lot of trees, spend time in a park, or even go lay down and stare at the sky somewhere. What's important is really keeping your attention on observing the natural world around you.

It can help bring a deep sense of gratitude for life itself.

"Gratitude is when memory is stored in the heart and not in the mind." - Lionel Hampton

I know my true worth, my true potential. I do what's right, not what's easy, to grow into that every day.

WHAT AM I GRATEFUL FOR TODAY?
(OPTIONAL THEME: ADVERSITY)

1. _____

2. _____

3. _____

WHAT MESSAGE DO I NEED TO REMIND MYSELF OF TODAY?

_____

_____

_____

HOW CAN I CHANGE MY MINDSET TO ATTRACT THE LIFE I TRULY WANT?

_____

_____

_____

IF I LOOKED AT MYSELF FROM THE PERSPECTIVE OF A CARE-GIVER, HOW WOULD I GUIDE MYSELF TO HAPPINESS?

_____

_____

MINI GRATITUDE ACTION OF THE DAY:

Completed?

HUG SOMEONE AND TAKE 3 FULL BREATHS. AS YOU DO IT, THINK ABOUT HOW SPECIAL THE PERSON IS. IF THERE'S NO ONE AROUND YOU TO DO THIS NOW, THINK OF SOMETHING YOU'RE PROUD OF YOURSELF FOR AND EMBRACE IT.

97

Day 23: **Daily Challenge**

Challenge: Carry a gratitude rock for a day.

We love the gratitude rock challenge.

The idea is this: Carry a small rock around in your pocket. Every time you feel the rock, immediately think of something you're grateful for and why.

That's it.

It's one of those simple exercises you can use to surprise yourself with gratitude. You never know when you're going to feel that rock, so when you do - regardless of the mood you're in, no matter what you're doing, you stop for a moment and find a sense of gratitude.

Exercises like this help provide a shock to your system because of the fact that it comes in surprise moments. It forces you to confront whatever you're feeling in a given moment and let it go so you can find a sense of gratitude.

It's awesome. Try it for a day and see how it impacts you!

☐ I completed this daily challenge.

"Stay connected to feel empathy, compassion, and understanding for yourself and others." - Vanessa Tucker

I search for the silver lining in bad situations. Even the most difficult times in my past have had beauty in them. I will remember this in the next tumultuous season.

WHAT AM I GRATEFUL FOR TODAY?
(OPTIONAL THEME: RELATIONSHIPS)

1. _____
2. _____
3. _____

WHAT MESSAGE DO I NEED TO REMIND MYSELF OF TODAY?

_____
_____
_____

IN WHAT WAYS COULD I BE WAY LESS FORTUNATE THAN I AM NOW?

_____
_____
_____

HOW COULD I SHIFT MY SELF-TALK TO BE MUCH MORE SUPPORTIVE, AS IF I WERE MY OWN BEST FRIEND?

_____
_____

MINI GRATITUDE ACTION OF THE DAY:

Completed?

THINK ABOUT THE WORST DAY YOU'VE EVER HAD. HOW DOES TODAY COMPARE?

☐

Day 24: **Affirmations**

1. Find a quiet area where you can do this in private so you can be at ease. If you can't find a private space, say this in your head while pretending you're screaming it from a mountaintop.

2. Think of a time when you felt absolutely powerful - **when you felt on top of the world.** Tap into every emotion you had at that moment and get yourself into that state right now. How were you feeling then - Powerful? Unstoppable? Strong? Incredible!? Get into it now!!!!

3. Now feel your intensity grow tenfold! Say this with deep passion:

All challenges are an opportunity for growth and I am thankful for the chance to evolve. I understand that growth is born out of discomfort, and I choose to see difficult circumstances as opportunities to deepen my gratitude practice and expand my sense of who I am.

Repeat this **one more time.**

"Humility is not about having a low self image or poor self esteem. Humility is about self-awareness." - Erwin McManus

Time is my friend. It is always there, always able to give to me as long as I am open to using it. I have extra hours in the morning, in the evening, and through the day.

WHAT AM I GRATEFUL FOR TODAY?
(OPTIONAL THEME: EVERY-DAY THINGS)

1. _____

2. _____

3. _____

WHAT MESSAGE DO I NEED TO REMIND MYSELF OF TODAY?

_____

_____

_____

WHAT AM I TAKING FOR GRANTED IN MY LIFE?

_____

_____

_____

WHAT'S SOMETHING I DID THAT I STILL REGRET? HOW CAN I EMPATHIZE WITH MYSELF FOR IT AND LEARN FROM IT INSTEAD?

_____

_____

MINI GRATITUDE ACTION OF THE DAY:

Completed?

DON'T COMPLAIN IF/WHEN SOMETHING 'BAD' OR 'ANNOYING' HAPPENS TODAY. INSTEAD, THINK OF ONE PROACTIVE THING YOU CAN DO TO MOVE FORWARD.

Day 25: **Food For Thought**

Nobody ever does anything they think is wrong... ever.

Have you ever, in your entire life, taken an action because you specifically thought that it was the wrong thing to do in that moment?

The answer is no. We never act because we think we're doing the WRONG thing. We always think what we're doing is right in the moment. 'Right' meaning that we think it'll lead to some desirable outcome, regardless of the consequences.

Aside from the rare exception, **_everyone is always doing their best in every moment_**, and the sooner we realize that, the more compassion and empathy we have for others and ourselves.

This doesn't mean that you can't grow, that you can't be better, that you can't change. It simply means that we're always making what we think is the emotionally right decision in a moment. We can be grateful for that in ourselves and in others, even if we later disagree with decisions made.

"We often take for granted the very things that most deserve our gratitude." - Cynthia Ozick

I am in control of my emotions. Others may poke at my soft-spots, but I know that I need not react. I am able to step out of my flustered mind and not react.

WHAT AM I GRATEFUL FOR TODAY?
(OPTIONAL THEME: MY BODY)

1. _____
2. _____
3. _____

WHAT MESSAGE DO I NEED TO REMIND MYSELF OF TODAY?

_____

_____

_____

KNOWING WHAT I KNOW TODAY, HOW WOULD I GUIDE MY YOUNGER SELF THROUGH A DIFFICULT SITUATION I WENT THROUGH?

_____

_____

_____

HOW COULD I BE MORE SUPPORTIVE OF MYSELF?

_____

_____

MINI GRATITUDE ACTION OF THE DAY:

Completed?

GO THROUGH YOUR CLOSET AND PUT ALL THE CLOTHES YOU NEVER WEAR IN A TRASH BAG. DONATE THOSE CLOTHES TO A PERSON YOU KNOW IN NEED, OR TO GOODWILL.

Day 26: **Daily Challenge** 🔥

Challenge: Eat a can of beans.

This challenge is a little bit dramatic, but it's very interesting and because of how dramatic it is, it works.

So many people in the world don't have the money to buy a can of beans without a lot of effort. We are SO lucky for the food we're able to put into our bodies without ever worrying where our next meal will come from.

The challenge is to buy a can of white beans, and for one meal, eat only that can of beans. Nothing added to it, no warming it up. Just open a can of beans, grab a spoon, and have it for lunch or dinner.

The purpose of the exercise is to really come into a deep sense of appreciation for the fact that we eat whatever we want whenever we want. It's so commonplace that we never think about it.

The exercise can be powerful, and if you're brave enough to try it, you are a rockstar.

"Be kind, for everyone you meet is fighting a hard battle." - Plato

I am not special. There is no one exactly like me, but my troubles are not unique to me. Someone has been where I am and has survived.

DATE _____

WHAT AM I GRATEFUL FOR TODAY?
(OPTIONAL THEME: COINCIDENCES)

1. _____

2. _____

3. _____

WHAT MESSAGE DO I NEED TO REMIND MYSELF OF TODAY?

_____

_____

_____

HOW DO I UTILIZE MY TALENTS AND ABILITIES IN WAYS I DON'T THINK ABOUT OR FULLY APPRECIATE?

_____

_____

_____

WHAT CAN I FORGIVE MYSELF FOR?

_____

_____

MINI GRATITUDE ACTION OF THE DAY:

Completed?

NEXT TIME YOU MAKE PLANS WITH FRIENDS OR FAMILY, INVITE SOMEONE YOU DON'T USUALLY INVITE WHO YOU KNOW WILL APPRECIATE THE INVITATION.

☐

Day 27: **Recommended Podcasts** 🎙️

The Gratitude Podcast with Georgian Benta

"Gratitude is the one thing that helped me most in my life from all the personal development and spiritual practices that I did and that's why I want to inspire 100.000 people to discover how to feel grateful more often and live a happy life. It's not happiness that makes us grateful; it's gratefulness that makes us happy." - Georgian Benta

Host Georgian Benta interviews successful people and gets them to share fascinating stories about how gratitude has helped them get to where they are now.

This is another insightful, story-filled podcast about gratitude that is well worth checking out!

One episode you might like is an interview with Jennifer Leigh called *How Vulnerability Leads to More Gratitude.*

The first step toward change is awareness. The second step is acceptance."
- Nathaniel Branden

I am my own best motivator. I know that motivation must be created and doesn't just happen on its own. I am strong enough to continue when my motivation wanes.

DATE

WHAT AM I GRATEFUL FOR TODAY?
(OPTIONAL THEME: WORK-RELATED)

1. _____
2. _____
3. _____

WHAT MESSAGE DO I NEED TO REMIND MYSELF OF TODAY?

_____

_____

_____

WHAT AM I HOLDING ONTO FROM MY PAST THAT IS HOLDING ME BACK?

_____

_____

_____

IN WHAT WAYS DOES THINKING ABOUT THE PAST STOP ME FROM IMPROVING IN THE FUTURE?

_____

_____

 ### MINI GRATITUDE ACTION OF THE DAY:

Completed?

WHO IS ALWAYS THERE FOR YOU WHEN YOU NEED THEM? WRITE THEM A THANK YOU NOTE! IF NO ONE COMES TO MIND, THIS CAN ALWAYS BE <u>YOU</u>!

107

Day 28: **Affirmations**

1. Find a quiet area where you can do this in private so you can be at ease. If you can't find a private space, say this in your head while pretending you're screaming it from a mountaintop.

2. Think of a time when you felt absolutely powerful - **when you felt on top of the world**. Tap into every emotion you had at that moment and get yourself into that state right now. How were you feeling then - Powerful? Unstoppable? Strong? Incredible!? Get into it now!!!!

3. Now feel your intensity grow tenfold! Say this with deep passion:

I am ready and grateful for the opportunity to learn from others. Each person I meet has valuable lessons to share, and rather than judge others for their mistakes or marvel at their achievements, I will incorporate their lessons to progress my own journey of life.

Repeat this **one more time.**

"I would maintain that thanks are the highest form of thought, and that gratitude is happiness doubled by wonder." - Gilbert C. Chesterton

I give myself permission to slow down. I do not need to accomplish everything today. My wellbeing and my relationships are exponentially _____ more important than completing tasks.

WHAT AM I GRATEFUL FOR TODAY?
(OPTIONAL THEME: NATURE)

1. _____

2. _____

3. _____

WHAT MESSAGE DO I NEED TO REMIND MYSELF OF TODAY?

_____

_____

_____

DOES REACTING NEGATIVELY EVER HELP A SITUATION I HAVE NO CHOICE BUT TO DEAL WITH? HOW CAN I SHIFT MY VIEW ON THINGS INSTEAD?

_____

_____

_____

HOW DOES MY MIND EXAGGERATE THE NEGATIVE WAYS I VIEW MYSELF?

_____

_____

MINI GRATITUDE ACTION OF THE DAY:

Completed?

TEXT A LOVED ONE AND ASK THEM WHAT ONE OF THEIR FAVORITE MEMORIES WITH YOU IS.

☐

Day 29: **Recommended Resource** 🍴

Watch this TedX Talk by David Steindl-Rast.

"The one thing all humans have in common is that each of us wants to be happy" says Brother David Steindl-Rast, a monk and interfaith scholar.

Happiness, he suggests, is born from gratitude. An inspiring lesson in slowing down, looking where you're going, and above all, being grateful.

This is an incredibly thought-provoking TedX talk. Brother David's demeanor and voice is so genuine, and what he shares is clearly from direct experience. It's a beautiful talk that everyone should watch.

You can check out the talk by searching for 'David Stendl Ted Talk' on YouTube or on the TED app!

"Empathy is a skill like any other human skill. If you get a chance to practice, you can get better at it." - Professor Simon Baron Cohen

I will let go of "what if." I know that worrying about possible outcomes will only rob me of joy. I will relinquish false control over these things. _____

WHAT AM I GRATEFUL FOR TODAY?
(OPTIONAL THEME: OPPORTUNITIES)

1. _____

2. _____

3. _____

WHAT MESSAGE DO I NEED TO REMIND MYSELF OF TODAY?

_____

_____

_____

WHAT BIG LIFE EVENT OR GOAL IS MY HAPPINESS ATTACHED TO?

_____

_____

_____

HOW CAN I TAKE MORE RESPONSIBILITY FOR MY OWN EMOTIONS AND BLAME OTHER PEOPLE OR EXTERNAL CIRCUMSTANCES LESS?

_____

_____

MINI GRATITUDE ACTION OF THE DAY:

Completed?

FIND THE (NON-EMERGENCY) PHONE # OF YOUR LOCAL POLICE OR FIRE DEPARTMENT AND CALL THEM TO THANK THEM FOR SERVING THE COMMUNITY. BONUS POINTS: BAKE TREATS AND DROP THEM OFF FOR THEM!

Day 30: **Food For Thought**

Validation from inside.

One of the really interesting things about us is that we very often don't feel like we've accomplished something until we get validation from the outside world and/or other people.

And it's awesome to get recognition for your achievements or the type of person you are.

But for some reason, it doesn't seem to be enough to feel good about something ourselves - it only really feels good when other people tell us about it or we're recognized publicly for it.

Gratitude for oneself - what one has accomplished and the qualities one respects about themselves - is the best gift we can give ourselves.

If you can really tap into feeling grateful for your own qualities and your own achievements, you no longer need validation from the outside world.

Very often, we are our own worst critic. Make it a goal to become your own best friend.

"What is necessary to change a person is to change his awareness of himself." - Abraham Maslow

I am guided by my own principles. I hold steadfast to my values and don't allow them to be compromised.

WHAT AM I GRATEFUL FOR TODAY?
(OPTIONAL THEME: MY OWN TALENTS & ABILITIES)

1. _____

2. _____

3. _____

WHAT MESSAGE DO I NEED TO REMIND MYSELF OF TODAY?

_____

_____

_____

IN WHAT WAYS DO MY PRECONCEIVED IDEAS OF WHO PEOPLE ARE AFFECT MY RELATIONSHIPS?

_____

_____

_____

HOW CAN I REMOVE GUILT FROM MY LIFE?

_____

_____

 ### MINI GRATITUDE ACTION OF THE DAY:

Completed?

THE NEXT TIME YOU DEAL WITH A CUSTOMER SERVICE REPRESENTATIVE WHO GOES ABOVE AND BEYOND, ASK THEM TO SPEAK WITH THEIR MANAGER AFTERWARDS AND LET THEM KNOW HOW GREAT OF A JOB THEIR EMPLOYEE DID.

☐

Day 31: **Affirmations**

1. Find a quiet area where you can do this in private so you can be at ease. If you can't find a private space, say this in your head while pretending you're screaming it from a mountaintop.

2. Think of a time when you felt absolutely powerful - **when you felt on top of the world**. Tap into every emotion you had at that moment and get yourself into that state right now. How were you feeling then - Powerful? Unstoppable? Strong? Incredible!? Get into it now!!!!

3. Now feel your intensity grow tenfold! Say this with deep passion:

There is no such thing as a perfect life. But my life is perfect just the way it is if I choose to see it as such because my life is perfectly suited to help me grow in the ways I know are necessary.

Repeat this **one more time.**

"Gratitude will shift you to a higher frequency, and you will attract much better things." - Rhonda Byrne

I am open to new experiences. I push fear away and seek out opportunities to experience as much of life as I can.

DATE _____

WHAT AM I GRATEFUL FOR TODAY?
(OPTIONAL THEME: EXPERIENCES)

1. _____
2. _____
3. _____

WHAT MESSAGE DO I NEED TO REMIND MYSELF OF TODAY?

_____

_____

_____

WHAT EXPERIENCE AM I GRATEFUL FOR, BUT AM GLAD IT IS OVER?

_____

_____

_____

WHY DO I JUDGE MYSELF SO HARSHLY?

_____

_____

MINI GRATITUDE ACTION OF THE DAY:

Completed?

WRITE A GENUINELY SUPPORTIVE, UPLIFTING COMMENT ON A SOCIAL MEDIA POST TODAY.

☐

Day 32: **Daily Challenge** ◊

Challenge: Verbally express your gratitude to someone today.

It can be really, really difficult and awkward to express genuine gratitude to somebody you care about - particularly to family members.

For some reason, it can just feel really weird to show emotion, vulnerability, and appreciation to the people closest to you.

The truth is that there is also nothing that feels better. The challenge today is to reach out to someone you are VERY close to in your life, and express your gratitude for them verbally. You can do it on the phone, but in person would be best.

The most important thing is to be authentic, and specific. Really express yourself to this person and help them understand how much of an impact they've had on you.

They will LIGHT UP, and you will be SO happy you took the leap.

☐ I completed this daily challenge.

"Compassion, empathy, and love are the real pillars we need to build within ourselves to become human." - Loknath

I am worthy of the income I bring in. I will live in gratitude for the financial opportunities I have and never take this for granted.

WHAT AM I GRATEFUL FOR TODAY?
(OPTIONAL THEME: TECHNOLOGY)

1. _____
2. _____
3. _____

WHAT MESSAGE DO I NEED TO REMIND MYSELF OF TODAY?

_____
_____
_____

WHAT WAS THE LAST NICE THING I DID FOR SOMEBODY?

_____
_____
_____

WHAT 'WRONG' CAN I 'RIGHT' WITH THE HELP OF GRATITUDE?

_____
_____

MINI GRATITUDE ACTION OF THE DAY:

Completed?

☐

THINK OF YOUR SENSE OF SMELL - WHERE WOULD YOU BE WITHOUT IT?
APPRECIATE YOUR NOSE FOR ALL IT DOES FOR YOU!

Day 33: **Daily Challenge**

**Challenge: Reflect on why you 'can't stand' someone.**

Think about someone in your life who you either have a difficult time with, or who has the capacity to simply annoy or bother you without actually doing much.

First, think about what it is about the person that really bothers you and write it down.

After, put that piece of paper aside, and grab a new one. Now, think about qualities this same person has that you genuinely appreciate.

What qualities does this person have that you admire? Is there anything about the way they live their life that you think is awesome?

So often we focus on others' negative qualities, we forget the beauty they bring to this world. Taking a little bit of time to remember even one awesome thing about someone you have a difficult time with can be eye-opening, and a great reminder that every one of us brings a different sort of beauty into this world.

☐ I completed this daily challenge.

UGH

INTERRUPTS ME WHEN I'M FOCUSED ON WORK.

INVITES HERSELF TO THINGS.

HAS THE LOUDEST, MOST JARRING LAUGH.

CAN'T "TAKE A HINT."

♥

WORKS REALLY HARD. REGULARLY ASKS ME IF SHE CAN TAKE THINGS OFF MY HANDS.

ALWAYS ASKS IF I WANT A COFFEE REFILL WHEN SHE'S GOING TO GET ONE.

ENJOYS MY JOKES.

JUST MOVED HERE... SHE PROBABLY DOESN'T HAVE MANY FRIENDS YET.

I refuse to allow others to impose their limitations on me. No one else is allowed to decide what I can or cannot do. I am capable of incredible, limitless things.

DATE _____

WHAT AM I GRATEFUL FOR TODAY?
(OPTIONAL THEME: ADVERSITY)

1. _____

2. _____

3. _____

WHAT MESSAGE DO I NEED TO REMIND MYSELF OF TODAY?

_____

_____

_____

HOW CAN I CHANGE MY MINDSET TO ATTRACT THE LIFE I TRULY WANT?

_____

_____

_____

IF I LOOKED AT MYSELF FROM THE PERSPECTIVE OF A CARE-GIVER, HOW WOULD I GUIDE MYSELF TO HAPPINESS?

_____

_____

 ### MINI GRATITUDE ACTION OF THE DAY:

Completed?

APPRECIATE YOUR SENSE OF SIGHT TODAY. HOW WOULD YOUR LIFE CHANGE IF YOU DIDN'T HAVE IT? WHAT HAVE YOU BEEN TAKING FOR GRANTED FROM IT?

☐

Day 34: **Food For Thought**

Gratitude isn't just a feeling.

Since the moment you were born, your heart hasn't stopped beating and circulating blood throughout your entire body. Every three seconds your body breathes without requiring any voluntary action on your part. Digestion, discharge of waste, perspiration, healing… the body does every instinctive process necessarily for life on its own.

The gift of life, in all its complexity and beauty, was and is continually given to us without asking for anything in return.

But what's clear is that we can impact the quality of our bodily processes by the way we choose to live. The way we eat, whether or not we exercise, whether we choose to give into stress and negativity… all of these things affect the efficiency with which our bodily processes take place. We're just beginning to scratch the surface of how emotions affect our body, but we know that there is a vital connection.

How can we show gratitude to our own bodies for this gift of life it is constantly giving us? Beyond feeling grateful and appreciating this wonderful mystery of a machine that we live in, how can our actions guide the gratitude we feel for our bodies?

"Gratitude helps you to grow and expand; gratitude brings joy and laughter into your life and into the lives of all those around you."
- Eileen Caddy

I will start tomorrow with a positive attitude, even if it doesn't feel natural. I will encourage myself to see the beauty beginning a new day.

WHAT AM I GRATEFUL FOR TODAY?
(OPTIONAL THEME: RELATIONSHIPS)

1. _____
2. _____
3. _____

WHAT MESSAGE DO I NEED TO REMIND MYSELF OF TODAY?

_____
_____
_____

IN WHAT WAYS COULD I BE WAY LESS FORTUNATE THAN I AM NOW?

_____
_____
_____

HOW COULD I SHIFT MY SELF-TALK TO BE MUCH MORE SUPPORTIVE, AS IF I WERE MY OWN BEST FRIEND?

_____
_____

MINI GRATITUDE ACTION OF THE DAY:

Completed?

STOP WHAT YOU'RE DOING AND JUST… LISTEN. HEAR THE WORLD AROUND YOU. APPRECIATE EVERY SOUND THAT COMES IN AND WHAT CAUSES IT FOR THE NEXT MINUTE. KNOW THAT YOU CAN DO THIS ANYTIME YOU NEED A BREATHER!

Day 35: **Pro-Tip**

What a 75-year Harvard study says is the key to a 'good life'

The Grant and Glueck studies have been tracking the physical and emotional wellbeing of two distinct groups of American males for 75 years. The Grant study was made up of 268 American males, all Harvard graduates in between 1939-1944. The Glueck study was composed of 456 men who grew up poor in Boston's inner cities.

The goal of the study was to examine whether any psychosocial and biological factors early in life could be identified to predict health and wellbeing much later in life.

Among the many findings that resulted, there is one clear indication of what leads to a 'good' life – and it isn't money or fame (any type of fame social or political).

"The clearest message that we get from this 75-year study is this: Good relationships keep us happier and healthier. Period."

One of the hallmarks of a 'good' relationship is a reciprocal gratitude for the relationship.

Foster your relationships. Share your appreciation in both words and actions, and do everything you can to maintain your relationships because it's the MOST important thing determining your quality of life.

THEN   NOW

"If you judge people, you have no time to love them." - Mother Teresa

I now let go of something that is dragging me down. I give it wholeheartedly to the universe and accept that it is only my issue if I allow it to be.

WHAT AM I GRATEFUL FOR TODAY?
(OPTIONAL THEME: EVERY-DAY THINGS)

1. _____
2. _____
3. _____

WHAT MESSAGE DO I NEED TO REMIND MYSELF OF TODAY?

_____

_____

_____

WHAT AM I TAKING FOR GRANTED IN MY LIFE?

_____

_____

_____

WHAT'S SOMETHING I DID THAT I STILL REGRET? HOW CAN I EMPATHIZE WITH MYSELF FOR IT AND LEARN FROM IT INSTEAD?

_____

_____

MINI GRATITUDE ACTION OF THE DAY:

Completed?

THE NEXT TIME YOU EAT, ENJOY THE FIRST 5 BITES OF YOUR MEAL AS MUCH AS YOU CAN. EAT THEM INCREDIBLY SLOWLY, TASTING EVERY INCH OF THE NOURISHING FOOD YOU'RE PUTTING INTO YOUR BODY.

123

Day 36: **YouTube Alert!**

Soulpancake.

3,000,000+ SUBSCRIBERS

Soulpancake is an awesome media and production company that believes in 'making stuff that matters.' Founded by Rainn Wilson (Dwight from 'The Office'), Soulpancake creates entertaining, joyful, meaningful video content for viewers to gain perspective in their lives and really make them think.

One of the BEST Soulpancake videos is a 'gratitude experiment'. Psychologists have scientifically proven that one of the biggest overall factors of happiness in your life is gratitude.

To test the impact of gratitude on happiness, they sat down a number of ordinary people and had them write a gratitude letter to one of the most influential people in their lives. After writing the letter, the participants had to call the person they wrote the letter for and read it to them aloud.

It's a beautiful, heartwarming video everyone should watch. It'll provide you the motivation you need to act on the Daily Challenge for Day 32 (if you haven't already)!

Soulpancake is one of those companies that's very easy to fall in love with.

You can check out the video described above by searching "Soulpancake gratitude experiment" on YouTube.

WE MAKE STUFF THAT MATTERS

"Awareness is a key ingredient in success. If you have it, teach it, if you lack it, seek it." - Michael B. Kitson

I am trustworthy. Others know that they will always be able to count on me. For this same reason, I trust MYSELF.

WHAT AM I GRATEFUL FOR TODAY?
(OPTIONAL THEME: MY BODY)

1. _____

2. _____

3. _____

WHAT MESSAGE DO I NEED TO REMIND MYSELF OF TODAY?

_____

_____

_____

KNOWING WHAT I KNOW TODAY, HOW WOULD I GUIDE MY YOUNGER SELF THROUGH A DIFFICULT SITUATION I WENT THROUGH?

_____

_____

_____

HOW COULD I BE MORE SUPPORTIVE OF MYSELF?

_____

_____

MINI GRATITUDE ACTION OF THE DAY:

Completed?

SIT DOWN AND FEEL YOUR SENSE OF TOUCH AGAINST THINGS AROUND YOU. PUT YOUR HAND OVER DIFFERENT PARTS OF YOUR BODY AND FEEL THE INCREDIBLE ABILITY WE HAVE AS HUMANS TO PERCEIVE TOUCH.

Day 37: **Daily Challenge**

Challenge: Volunteer for a day.

Think about how much time every single one of us spends unwinding, relaxing, messing around on social media, watching TV, etc. Probably at least a couple of hours a day for most of us.

And there is nothing wrong with that. The point we'd like to make is that we all have time to volunteer and spend time doing something good that isn't for ourselves or the people closest to us.

Volunteering is one of the best ways to find and experience gratitude in your own life. Not only does it become an incredible reminder of how fortunate you are, but it feels even better to do something awesome that is going to impact other lives.

There are an unlimited number of volunteer opportunities and causes to support with your effort. You will never, ever regret volunteering!

1. Choose a cause you're passionate about.
2. Find an opportunity that matches your skills and interests.
3. Make the time and do it, no matter how short or long.

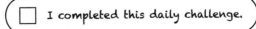

☐ I completed this daily challenge.

"Two kinds of gratitude: The sudden kind we feel for what we take; the larger kind we feel for what we give." - Edwin Arlington Robinson

I am happy. I have a roof over my head, food on my table, and love in my heart. I need nothing more from life than this.

WHAT AM I GRATEFUL FOR TODAY?
(OPTIONAL THEME: COINCIDENCES)

1. _____
2. _____
3. _____

WHAT MESSAGE DO I NEED TO REMIND MYSELF OF TODAY?

_____

_____

_____

HOW DO I UTILIZE MY TALENTS AND ABILITIES IN WAYS I DON'T THINK ABOUT OR FULLY APPRECIATE?

_____

_____

_____

WHAT CAN I FORGIVE MYSELF FOR?

_____

_____

MINI GRATITUDE ACTION OF THE DAY:

Completed?

GO PLAY ONE OF YOUR FAVORITE SONGS RIGHT NOW AND GIVE YOUR WHOLE HEART TO ENJOYING AND JAMMING OUT TO IT!

Day 38: **Recommended Podcasts** 🎙️

Morning Mindfulness with Dr. Jin

Morning Mindfulness is hosted by Dr. Jin. This is how he describes his podcast:

"This podcast is about mindfulness. It is about being in the moment. It is about paying attention. It is about nonjudgmental attitude. It is about awareness. It is about making wiser decisions. I am talking about lessons I've learned on my Martial Arts and Yoga journey, and what I've learned practicing meditation. My episodes are inspired by lessons I got from World's greatest success and leadership teachers."

Each one of his podcast episodes are only a few minutes long, but are packed with inspiration. He usually tells a story or fable with a poignant lesson.

Because each episode is so short, there's no excuse to get your daily dose of wisdom.

Mindfulness and gratitude are delicately intertwined. You can only be grateful right now, in this moment.

Check him out!

I am a do-er. I will pay attention to the things I procrastinate on and commit myself to tackling them.

WHAT AM I GRATEFUL FOR TODAY?
(OPTIONAL THEME: WORK-RELATED)

1. _____

2. _____

3. _____

WHAT MESSAGE DO I NEED TO REMIND MYSELF OF TODAY?

_____

_____

_____

WHAT AM I HOLDING ONTO FROM MY PAST THAT IS HOLDING ME BACK?

_____

_____

_____

IN WHAT WAYS DOES THINKING ABOUT THE PAST STOP ME FROM IMPROVING IN THE FUTURE?

_____

_____

MINI GRATITUDE ACTION OF THE DAY:

Completed?

WHAT HAS RECENTLY BEEN A BLESSING IN DISGUISE? HOW DID YOUR PERSPECTIVE CHANGE FROM WHEN IT FIRST HAPPENED TO NOW?

☐

Day 39: **Pro-Tip**

Save positive social media posts.

Make social media work in favor of developing your habit of gratitude.

How?

By saving any social media post that makes you smile of joy, gives you the chills because it is deeply insightful, cry of warmth and authenticity, helps you understand how fortunate you are for your life, or makes you laugh so hard it makes you pee in your pants just a little bit.

Over time, you'll create a library of posts you can turn back to whenever you need a pick-me up!

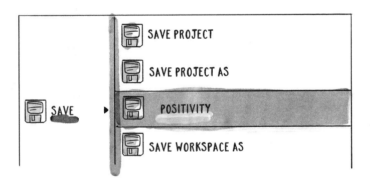

"Being self-aware is not the absence of mistakes, but the ability to learn and correct them." - Daniel Chidiac

I am proud of myself. I have worked hard for what I have and it shows! My life didn't just 'happen' to me; I worked with the ups and downs to get myself here

WHAT AM I GRATEFUL FOR TODAY?
(OPTIONAL THEME: NATURE)

1. _____
2. _____
3. _____

WHAT MESSAGE DO I NEED TO REMIND MYSELF OF TODAY?

_____

_____

_____

DOES REACTING NEGATIVELY EVER HELP A SITUATION I HAVE NO CHOICE BUT TO DEAL WITH? HOW CAN I SHIFT MY VIEW ON THINGS INSTEAD?

_____

_____

_____

HOW DOES MY MIND EXAGGERATE THE NEGATIVE WAYS I VIEW MYSELF?

_____

_____

MINI GRATITUDE ACTION OF THE DAY:

Completed?

COMPLIMENT SOMEONE PUBLICLY (I.E. IN A GROUP SETTING) IN A WAY THAT WILL MAKE THEM FEEL GREAT.

☐

Day 40: **Daily Challenge** 🔥

Challenge: Start a gratitude jar.

One of the more popular and simple ways to foster the habit of gratitude in your daily life is to start filling up a gratitude jar.

Here's how you can do it:

1. Find an empty jar.
2. Choose 1-3 specific times a day during which you'll write something you're grateful for on a small piece of paper or post it note.
3. Write your gratitude notes and put them in the jar.
4. When it's filled up, empty the jar, read through all your notes, and begin again.

It's a simple daily action you can take that'll force you to pause and find gratitude before moving onto the rest of your day. Try writing one note in the morning before you leave your home and one at night right before going to bed. These are both great times to write your notes for consistency.

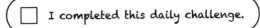

I completed this daily challenge.

I feel the presence of my loved ones, even if they aren't here. I am in tune with nature and spirit and know that there is more to life than what I see.

WHAT AM I GRATEFUL FOR TODAY?
(OPTIONAL THEME: OPPORTUNITIES)

1. _____

2. _____

3. _____

WHAT MESSAGE DO I NEED TO REMIND MYSELF OF TODAY?

_____

_____

_____

WHAT BIG LIFE EVENT OR GOAL IS MY HAPPINESS ATTACHED TO?

_____

_____

_____

HOW CAN I TAKE MORE RESPONSIBILITY FOR MY OWN EMOTIONS AND BLAME OTHER PEOPLE OR EXTERNAL CIRCUMSTANCES LESS?

_____

_____

 MINI GRATITUDE ACTION OF THE DAY:

Completed?

THINK OF A MOMENT WHEN YOU WERE IN AWE AS A CHILD. HOW CAN YOU BRING THAT ELEMENT OF CHILDLIKE WONDER TO ONE ASPECT OF YOUR LIFE TODAY?

☐

133

Day 41: **Pro-Tip**

<u>*Replace complaints with blessings.*</u>

Our aim isn't simply to feel more grateful, but to use gratitude as a way to transform our emotional life.

Gratitude and negativity cannot co-exist.

Two contradictory thoughts cannot consume the same space in your mind the same way two physical objects can't take up the same space.

Incorporating a demeanor of gratitude into the way you are is a process that literally requires changing how your brain operates.

One way to facilitate that process is to stop yourself every time you find yourself complaining inside of your head, and replace the thought with one that incorporates gratitude into the moment. It's a big part of the process of 're-wiring' how you think.

Over time, if you stay consistent, the natural tendency will move from negative thoughts and negative reactions, to positive, grateful ones.

"I believe empathy is the most essential quality of civilization."
- Roger Ebert

I breathe in calmness and breathe out anxiety. I know that I can ground myself in this world to drive away the panic and fear that sometimes creeps into my mind.

DATE _____

WHAT AM I GRATEFUL FOR TODAY?
(OPTIONAL THEME: MY OWN TALENTS & ABILITIES)

1. _____

2. _____

3. _____

WHAT MESSAGE DO I NEED TO REMIND MYSELF OF TODAY?

_____

_____

_____

IN WHAT WAYS DO MY PRECONCEIVED IDEAS OF WHO PEOPLE ARE AFFECT MY RELATIONSHIPS?

_____

_____

_____

HOW CAN I REMOVE GUILT FROM MY LIFE?

_____

_____

MINI GRATITUDE ACTION OF THE DAY:

Completed?

IN A CONVERSATION TODAY, PLACE AN EMPHASIS ON LISTENING MORE THAN YOU SPEAK, EVEN IF WHAT YOU HAVE TO SAY WOULD BE HELPFUL.
OFTENTIMES PURE, UNBRIDLED ATTENTION CAN HELP MORE THAN ANY INPUT.

☐

Day 42: **Recommended Podcasts** 🎙️
Life is a Marathon with Bruce Van Horn.

Bruce Van Horn is a Transformational Life Coach, Mentor, Thought Leader, Best-Selling Author, Empowering and Motivational Speaker, Dad, and Marathon runner.

He brings his respected insight, wisdom, perspective, thought leadership, and storytelling abilities to this podcast to share information, life training tips, and entertaining and heart-warming stories. His goal is to help transform people's ordinary lives into extraordinary ones — to build self-esteem, to help people recognize their value to the world, and to help them live as the fullest expression of who they were created to be.

Your thinking defines who you are in every way. Your mindset, how you think about yourself, others, and the world around you, effects your self-esteem, self-image, and self-worth. It also controls the way you perceive the world and how you interact with others. You can change your life by changing your thoughts. Use this podcast as your personal mentoring program as you transform your life by the renewing of your mind.

One episode we love is Episode 478 - "Your word is your superpower."

I forgive myself for my mistakes. I am not a perfect human being. I learn from my slip-ups and give myself grace.

DATE

WHAT AM I GRATEFUL FOR TODAY?
(OPTIONAL THEME: EXPERIENCES)

1. _____

2. _____

3. _____

WHAT MESSAGE DO I NEED TO REMIND MYSELF OF TODAY?

_____

_____

_____

WHAT EXPERIENCE AM I GRATEFUL FOR, BUT AM GLAD IT IS OVER?

_____

_____

_____

WHY DO I JUDGE MYSELF SO HARSHLY?

_____

_____

MINI GRATITUDE ACTION OF THE DAY:

Completed?

THINK OF ONE PERSONALITY TRAIT YOU WERE BORN WITH THAT YOU LOVE ABOUT YOURSELF. HOW HAS THIS POSITIVELY AFFECTED PEOPLE AROUND YOU IN YOUR LIFE?

Day 43: **Affirmations**

1. Find a quiet area where you can do this in private so you can be
   at ease. If you can't find a private space, say this in your head
   while pretending you're screaming it from a mountaintop.

2. Think of a time when you felt absolutely powerful - **when you
   felt on top of the world**. Tap into every emotion you had at that
   moment and get yourself into that state right now. How were you
   feeling then - Powerful? Unstoppable? Strong? Incredible!? Get
   into it now!!!!

3. Now feel your intensity grow tenfold! Say this with deep passion:

---

*I cannot change anybody else, but I can make a concrete decision to
accept each person for who they are. I am grateful for the positive
qualities I find in the people around me. I am grateful for what I
believe are negative qualities in those around me. I choose empathy for
others over judgment and criticism.*

Repeat this **one more time.**

"The more grateful I am, the more beauty I see." - Mary Davis

138

I forgive others who have wronged me. I know that holding on to hurt feelings only dwindles my own energy.

DATE _____

♡ WHAT AM I GRATEFUL FOR TODAY?
(OPTIONAL THEME: TECHNOLOGY)

1. _____

2. _____

3. _____

WHAT MESSAGE DO I NEED TO REMIND MYSELF OF TODAY?

_____

_____

_____

WHAT WAS THE LAST NICE THING I DID FOR SOMEBODY?

_____

_____

_____

WHAT 'WRONG' CAN I 'RIGHT' WITH THE HELP OF GRATITUDE?

_____

_____

MINI GRATITUDE ACTION OF THE DAY:

Completed?

FLIP BACK TO AN EARLIER PAGE IN THIS BOOK AND READ WHAT YOU WROTE. IN WHAT WAYS HAVE YOU GROWN SINCE THEN?

☐

Day 44: **Food For Thought**

Butterfly vs. Bee

When you see a butterfly flying around on a sunny day, you can't help but feel a warm opening inside of you. You welcome the butterfly emotionally, and you're usually so glad to see it. It's always a wonderful surprise that brings warmth into your experience, even if just for a moment.

When you see a bee, especially when it comes close to you, you usually close up. It's like you emotionally reject the bee because you're thrown into fight or flight mode and the only thing you want in the world is for that bee to leave you alone.

It's incredible what a drastic difference it makes in terms of what we experience when we see a bee vs. when we see a butterfly. But how many times have you really been stung by a bee? Once? Twice?

If you examine yourself a little more closely, you'll see that the only real difference is the way you perceive each of these insects. Your response is conditioned based on what you've always thought when you see or come in contact with each one.

Our perception is EVERYTHING. Next time you see a bee, try to see what happens inside of you, and see if you can prevent from closing up. Rather than close emotionally and feel fear, try to open and think of the bee as another living being. See if it changes your experience!

I trust my own wisdom in decision making.
Large or small, I make decisions every single
day that are the right ones.

WHAT AM I GRATEFUL FOR TODAY?
(OPTIONAL THEME: ADVERSITY)

1. _____

2. _____

3. _____

WHAT MESSAGE DO I NEED TO REMIND MYSELF OF TODAY?

_____

_____

_____

HOW CAN I CHANGE MY MINDSET TO ATTRACT THE LIFE I TRULY WANT?

_____

_____

_____

IF I LOOKED AT MYSELF FROM THE PERSPECTIVE OF A CARE-GIVER, HOW WOULD I GUIDE MYSELF TO HAPPINESS?

_____

_____

MINI GRATITUDE ACTION OF THE DAY:

Completed?

WRITE A GRATITUDE LETTER / EMAIL TO A FAMILY MEMBER OR LOVED ONE AND SEND IT TO THEM A MONTH FROM NOW. INCLUDE THE DATE IT WAS WRITTEN AND HOW THANKFUL YOU ARE FOR EVERYTHING THEY'VE BROUGHT INTO YOUR LIFE.

Day 45: **Pro-Tip**

**Make yourself as happy as possible.**

Gratitude and happiness feed off one another. Being grateful can facilitate happiness, and when you're happy, it facilitates gratitude.

So one way to increase your sense of gratitude for your own life is to try and live in ways that naturally make you happy.

Do things that make you happy. Spend time with people who make you smile. Be adventurous, have good food, go on a walk, learn new things, binge watch a TV show with a friend… do anything that makes you happy as often as you can.

Because the happier you are, the more grateful you become. The more grateful you become, the more you enjoy life. The more you enjoy life, the more you perceive the events of your life positively, no matter what they are.

"Awareness is all about restoring your freedom to choose what you want instead of what your past imposes on you." - Deepak Chopra

I express love and gratitude to my family. I make it a point to foster these healthy relationships.

WHAT AM I GRATEFUL FOR TODAY?
(OPTIONAL THEME: RELATIONSHIPS)

1. _____

2. _____

3. _____

WHAT MESSAGE DO I NEED TO REMIND MYSELF OF TODAY?

_____

_____

_____

IN WHAT WAYS COULD I BE WAY LESS FORTUNATE THAN I AM NOW?

_____

_____

_____

HOW COULD I SHIFT MY SELF-TALK TO BE MUCH MORE SUPPORTIVE, AS IF I WERE MY OWN BEST FRIEND?

_____

_____

MINI GRATITUDE ACTION OF THE DAY:

Completed?

IF YOU'RE IN ANY LINE TO BUY FOOD/DRINKS, PAY FOR THE NEXT PERSON'S BILL WITHOUT ANY EXPECTATION OF ANYTHING IN RETURN.

143

Day 46: **Food For Thought**

1 in 400 trillion

Scientists estimate that the probability of being born is 1 to 400 trillion.

To put that into perspective, the odds of being struck by lightning are 1/700,000, and the odds of winning the lottery are 1/14,000,000.

Think about exactly what had to happen for you to be alive and reading this right now - everybody, since the beginning of time, who had to meet and have children for you to be here living your life. All the favorable conditions that were necessary.

The good fortune that needed to take place for everything to work out perfectly so that your parents met and birthed the miracle that you are.

You are, quite literally, a miracle.

"Gratitude is the most exquisite form of courtesy." - Jacques Maritain

I am able to say goodbye. I know that sometimes, relationships aren't healthy, even if they are family. It takes a lot for me to say goodbye, so when I feel this way, it is important to listen to my heart.

DATE _____

WHAT AM I GRATEFUL FOR TODAY?
(OPTIONAL THEME: EVERY-DAY THINGS)

1. _____

2. _____

3. _____

WHAT MESSAGE DO I NEED TO REMIND MYSELF OF TODAY?

_____

_____

_____

WHAT AM I TAKING FOR GRANTED IN MY LIFE?

_____

_____

_____

WHAT'S SOMETHING I DID THAT I STILL REGRET? HOW CAN I EMPATHIZE WITH MYSELF FOR IT AND LEARN FROM IT INSTEAD?

_____

_____

 MINI GRATITUDE ACTION OF THE DAY:

Completed?

THINK OF SOMETHING YOU MAY DO IN THE FUTURE THAT YOU'LL BE VERY CRITICAL OF YOURSELF FOR. MAKE A PACT NOW THAT YOU'LL BE RIDICULOUSLY EMPOWERING AND SUPPORTIVE INSTEAD.

☐

Day 47: **Daily Challenge**

Challenge: Create a gratitude board.

A fun way to work with your gratitude habit is to make a gratitude board.

You can take the challenge of making a gratitude board in a number of ways. Similarly to a gratitude jar, you can create and design a board that you hang up somewhere in your home or place of work, and choose a time each day on which you'll write a note about what you're grateful for.

You can also make this a one-time project. Here's how:

1. Get a board.
2. Choose 5 categories of things you want to focus on your gratitude for.
3. Divide the board to have space for all 5 categories.
4. Start filling the board in with pictures, notes, quotes, jokes.. anything that helps remind you what you're grateful for within the topics you chose. Design it, and make it fun!

Keep the board somewhere you'll see it every day as a visual reminder of how much you have to be grateful for.

> ☐ I completed this daily challenge.

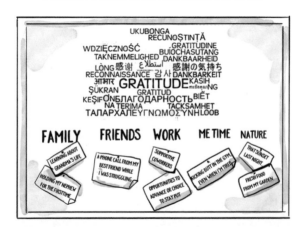

I surround myself with people who treat me the way I deserve to be treated. I also recognize that sometimes, I need to be told some hard truths and my friends may be the voice of this.

♡ WHAT AM I GRATEFUL FOR TODAY?
(OPTIONAL THEME: MY BODY)

1. _____

2. _____

3. _____

WHAT MESSAGE DO I NEED TO REMIND MYSELF OF TODAY?

_____

_____

_____

KNOWING WHAT I KNOW TODAY, HOW WOULD I GUIDE MY YOUNGER SELF THROUGH A DIFFICULT SITUATION I WENT THROUGH?

_____

_____

_____

HOW COULD I BE MORE SUPPORTIVE OF MYSELF?

_____

_____

MINI GRATITUDE ACTION OF THE DAY:

Completed?

LET'S GET NOSTALGIC - THINK OF A STORY WITH SOMEONE FROM YOUR CHILDHOOD THAT STILL BRINGS YOU JOY OR LAUGHTER TO THIS DAY. LET THAT PERSON KNOW HOW MUCH YOU ENJOYED THAT MOMENT WITH THEM!

☐

147

Day 48: **Recommended Resource** 🍴

Watch AJ Jacobs' TedX Talk about his 'thank you' journey.

Author AJ Jacobs is a journalist, lecturer, self-proclaimed guinea pig, and author of four New York Times bestsellers. AJ is an interesting author because his books involve a self-journey he later writes about.

His latest book, *'Thanks a Thousand'*, is about his journey to thank everybody involved in creating his morning cup of coffee.

More than one thousand 'thank yous' later, Jacobs reflects on the globe-trotting journey that ensued -- and shares the life-altering wisdom he picked up along the way.

He talks about how this gratitude journey impacted his life and shares all the lessons he learns in a wonderful Ted Talk.

You can access the TedX Talk by searching for "AJ Jacobs TedX Talk" on YouTube or the TED app!

"As our awareness grows, so we grow." - Anonymous

I am confident in social situations. I know that I can always leave if I choose to. I also know that I could meet someone fascinating if _____

WHAT AM I GRATEFUL FOR TODAY?
(OPTIONAL THEME: COINCIDENCES)

1. _____

2. _____

3. _____

WHAT MESSAGE DO I NEED TO REMIND MYSELF OF TODAY?

_____

_____

_____

HOW DO I UTILIZE MY TALENTS AND ABILITIES IN WAYS I DON'T THINK ABOUT OR FULLY APPRECIATE?

_____

_____

_____

WHAT CAN I FORGIVE MYSELF FOR?

_____

_____

MINI GRATITUDE ACTION OF THE DAY:

Completed?

RIGHT NOW — SET A 3 MINUTE TIMER ON YOUR PHONE, CLOSE YOUR EYES, AND THINK ABOUT EACH POSITIVE THING THAT YOU GOT TO EXPERIENCE TODAY.

Day 49: **YouTube Alert!**

watchwellcast.

900,000+ SUBSCRIBERS ▶

Watchwellcast is an awesome YouTube channel that, for just one year, made dozens of short, animated videos that explore the physical, mental, and emotional paths to wellness.

The show addressed the latest trends and long-standing practices of wellness-everything from the efficacy of gratitude experiments to the importance of daily sunlight.

Oh, and they even guide you through a journaling exercise to apply what they teach you. This channel was created six years ago, and all of their videos are still on YouTube. It's fun to watch, and there are life lessons jam-packed into each one.

One episode you'll like is "The Gratitude Experiment," discussing the Hedonic treadmill that we mentioned in the introduction to this journal, along with other science behind how gratitude makes you happier.

You can check out the episode by searching "watchwellcast the gratitude experiment" on YouTube.

"The root of joy is gratefulness." - David Steindl-Rast

I push away false stories I have concocted in my mind. I recognize that the way I see the scenario and what actually played out are unlikely to be the same thing.

WHAT AM I GRATEFUL FOR TODAY?
(OPTIONAL THEME: WORK-RELATED)

1. _____

2. _____

3. _____

WHAT MESSAGE DO I NEED TO REMIND MYSELF OF TODAY?

_____

_____

_____

WHAT AM I HOLDING ONTO FROM MY PAST THAT IS HOLDING ME BACK?

_____

_____

_____

IN WHAT WAYS DOES THINKING ABOUT THE PAST STOP ME FROM IMPROVING IN THE FUTURE?

_____

_____

MINI GRATITUDE ACTION OF THE DAY:

Completed?

CHALLENGE YOURSELF TO THINK "THIS IS AN OPPORTUNITY" INSTEAD OF DWELLING ON ANY DIFFICULT/ANNOYING SITUATION THAT MAY ARISE TODAY.

151

Day 50: **Food For Thought**

Money isn't the answer.

Purdue University published a study in 2018 in which researchers found that $105,000 is the ideal income for life satisfaction in North America. Earnings past the $105,000 mark seemed to be linked to lower levels of happiness and well-being.

Once basic needs are met, money becomes more about the chase, and about comparing what you have to others, which ultimately does not result in more happiness.

Moreover, we tend to very quickly get used to our new financial status when we have rises in income, with our happiness leveling off to its usual, stable place.

Never forget that having money is not an end in itself.

Money has no value outside of the fact that it can allow you to continue DOING what you enjoy - what gives you meaning - and it can continue to help others do what they enjoy and gives them meaning.

HAPPINESS

"Empathy is a special way of coming to know another and ourself."
- Carl R. Rogers

I choose to participate 100% tomorrow. I will not cut corners or avoid anything. I will prove to myself that more energy is spent in avoiding than participating.

DATE

WHAT AM I GRATEFUL FOR TODAY?
(OPTIONAL THEME: NATURE)

1. _____

2. _____

3. _____

WHAT MESSAGE DO I NEED TO REMIND MYSELF OF TODAY?

_____

_____

_____

DOES REACTING NEGATIVELY EVER HELP A SITUATION I HAVE NO CHOICE BUT TO DEAL WITH? HOW CAN I SHIFT MY VIEW ON THINGS INSTEAD?

_____

_____

_____

HOW DOES MY MIND EXAGGERATE THE NEGATIVE WAYS I VIEW MYSELF?

_____

_____

 ### MINI GRATITUDE ACTION OF THE DAY:

Completed?

PHYSICAL TENSION IS A BIG WEIGHT WE CARRY ON OUR SHOULDERS, OFTEN LITERALLY! CAN YOU GIVE SOMEONE YOU'RE CLOSE WITH A MASSAGE TODAY?

Day 51: **Daily Challenge**

**Challenge: Get someone else on the gratitude wagon!**

One way to hold yourself accountable to making a positive change is by having a partner alongside you, but the ULTIMATE form of accountability is seeing success in yourself and THEN encouraging others to adopt the same positive behavior.

When you preach, you have basically no choice but to practice. You're on Day 51 of this journal - regardless of how close or far you are from your ultimate goal, you've come an insanely long way towards incorporating gratitude into your life as a daily practice.

Choose a friend or loved one you know needs the inspiration and knowledge you've gained. Motivate them through your own story and help them understand that they TOO can realize the benefits you've begun to receive.

You have the power to change other people's lives which will motivate you to continue on your own path of change.

☐ I completed this daily challenge.

"Once you become aware of what you are capable of achieving, you won't settle for mediocrity." - Anonymous

I see beauty in the imperfect. I recognize that nothing will ever be exactly the way I want, but I will always be able to find the good if I chose to look.

WHAT AM I GRATEFUL FOR TODAY?
(OPTIONAL THEME: OPPORTUNITIES)

1. _____
2. _____
3. _____

WHAT MESSAGE DO I NEED TO REMIND MYSELF OF TODAY?

_____

_____

_____

WHAT BIG LIFE EVENT OR GOAL IS MY HAPPINESS ATTACHED TO?

_____

_____

_____

HOW CAN I TAKE MORE RESPONSIBILITY FOR MY OWN EMOTIONS AND BLAME OTHER PEOPLE OR EXTERNAL CIRCUMSTANCES LESS?

_____

_____

 ### MINI GRATITUDE ACTION OF THE DAY:

Completed?

PAY CLOSE ATTENTION TO WATER TODAY, PARTICULARLY HOW MUCH IT BENEFITS YOUR HEALTH AND WELLBEING. FEEL GRATEFUL THAT YOU HAVE SUCH EASY ACCESS TO IT EVERY SINGLE DAY OF YOUR LIFE.

☐

Day 52: **Affirmations**

1. Find a quiet area where you can do this in private so you can be at ease. If you can't find a private space, say this in your head while pretending you're screaming it from a mountaintop.

2. Think of a time when you felt absolutely powerful - **when you felt on top of the world.** Tap into every emotion you had at that moment and get yourself into that state right now. How were you feeling then - Powerful? Unstoppable? Strong? Incredible!? Get into it now!!!!

3. Now feel your intensity grow tenfold! Say this with deep passion:

There is so much beauty in the world around me. I don't ignore the small reminders that nature expresses to me about the wonder of the world.

Repeat this **one more time.**

"Gratitude unlocks the fullness of life. It turns what we have into enough, and more. It turns denial into acceptance, chaos to order, confusion to clarity. It can turn a meal into a feast, a house into a home, a stranger into a friend." - Melody Beattie

I am beautiful. I'm beautiful on the inside. I am beautiful on the outside. I am a model for _____ what a beautiful person is.

WHAT AM I GRATEFUL FOR TODAY?
(OPTIONAL THEME: MY OWN TALENTS & ABILITIES)

1. _____
2. _____
3. _____

WHAT MESSAGE DO I NEED TO REMIND MYSELF OF TODAY?

_____

_____

_____

IN WHAT WAYS DO MY PRECONCEIVED IDEAS OF WHO PEOPLE ARE AFFECT MY RELATIONSHIPS?

_____

_____

_____

HOW CAN I REMOVE GUILT FROM MY LIFE?

_____

_____

MINI GRATITUDE ACTION OF THE DAY:

Completed?

BUY 3 POSTCARDS AND WRITE A SHORT NOTE TO 3 DIFFERENT PEOPLE. INCLUDE A FAVORITE MEMORY, A FUNNY MOMENT, OR APPRECIATION FOR THEM. MAIL THEM... DON'T LET THEM SIT ON YOUR COUNTER!

157

Day 53: **Recommended Resource** 🍴

**Watch Katia Sol's TedX talk on the transformative power of gratitude.**

In the talk, leadership and education expert Katia Sol discusses how gratitude is an ancient 'technology' which many are just now identifying the power of, and explores some of the recent research into gratitude, including some of Robert Emmons's work.

The 20 minute talk is a deep exploration into the transformative power of gratitude from both a practical and scientific standpoint.

You can check out the talk by searching 'Katia Sol TedX Talk' on YouTube or on the TED app!

GRATITUDE
TRANSFORMS

"Leadership is about empathy. It is about having the ability to relate to and connect with people for the purpose of inspiring and empowering their lives." - Oprah Winfrey

I am resilient. I face obstacles all day long, all throughout my life, and I keep moving forward.

_____
DATE

WHAT AM I GRATEFUL FOR TODAY?
(OPTIONAL THEME: EXPERIENCES)

1. _____
2. _____
3. _____

WHAT MESSAGE DO I NEED TO REMIND MYSELF OF TODAY?

_____

_____

_____

WHAT EXPERIENCE AM I GRATEFUL FOR, BUT AM GLAD IT IS OVER?

_____

_____

_____

WHY DO I JUDGE MYSELF SO HARSHLY?

_____

_____

MINI GRATITUDE ACTION OF THE DAY:

Completed?

GIVE A CASH TIP TO SOMEONE WHO LEAST EXPECTS IT. FAST FOOD WORKERS, IN PARTICULAR, RARELY RECEIVE TIPS AND FREQUENTLY DEAL WITH DIFFICULT PEOPLE. $5 CAN ABSOLUTELY LIGHT UP SOMEONE'S FACE!

☐

Day 54: **Pro-Tip**

Small negative reactions have chain effects on your day.

Reacting negatively to things like sitting in traffic, a snarky comment from a co-worker, getting a ticket, or having to do something you weren't planning for, all have compounding effects further into your life's future.

Very commonly, yet unknowingly, these smaller reactions lead to a chain of effects that will negatively effect us. Reacting negatively to sitting in traffic affects my mood, which affects my actions. When I get home, I'll probably be a little more short with my family, partner, or roommate. If I get a call, I'll have an attitude that isn't welcoming.

And my emotions are contagious to those around me - whoever I speak to can feel the negativity I'm feeling and maybe they'll react poorly to my negativity, or carry it on into their life because now, I've infected them with it.

Feeling negative changes how you behave, the decisions you make... it changes everything. And we have no idea how far the effect goes, but we do know that it is contagious. Keep this chain of effects in mind when you find yourself reacting negatively to things, especially things that clearly don't matter and are out of your control. A poor reaction can lead to a whole series of terrible unforeseen events that did not need to take place.

"Who looks outside, dreams; who looks inside, awakes." - Carl Jung

I am intelligent. I have the ability to know right from wrong and contribute positively to conversations and interactions.

WHAT AM I GRATEFUL FOR TODAY?
(OPTIONAL THEME: TECHNOLOGY)

1. _____

2. _____

3. _____

WHAT MESSAGE DO I NEED TO REMIND MYSELF OF TODAY?

_____

_____

_____

WHAT WAS THE LAST NICE THING I DID FOR SOMEBODY?

_____

_____

_____

WHAT 'WRONG' CAN I 'RIGHT' WITH THE HELP OF GRATITUDE?

_____

_____

MINI GRATITUDE ACTION OF THE DAY:

Completed?

SMILE GENUINELY AT EVERYONE YOU SEE TODAY. YOU MAY FEEL STRANGE AT FIRST, BUT AFTER A WHILE, YOU'LL GET COMFORTABLE. PAY ATTENTION TO HOW OTHERS' DEMEANOR CHANGES WHEN YOU'VE SMILED AT THEM.

☐

Day 55: **Food For Thought**

A beautiful Medium blog post about gratitude.

"I look at gratitude as a mirror. One in which I can see myself as I really am and show gratitude with all that I offer. In this mirror, I find relationships, both past and present, clearly outlined for me to appreciate.

When you are looking through this mirror with clarity, there is an understanding of both positive and uncomfortable elements in your life. There is equanimity in your graciousness, because you know life isn't always easy. You don't curse the universe for a bad hair day because you feel gratitude that you have hair on your beautiful head.

When we disconnect from the emotion of it all, we have an opportunity to look at life from the perspective of an outsider. The problems that were illuminated become dim and instead we are left with the abundance that is life."

- Ava Pendl, mindfulness advocate, yoga x meditation x breathwork teacher, host of The Alchemized Life Podcast

"Today I choose to live with gratitude for the love that fills my heart, the peace that rests within my spirit, and the voice of hope that says all things are possible." - Anonymous

I am a magnet for good things. I put out good things into the world and find that many times, _____ good things come back.

WHAT AM I GRATEFUL FOR TODAY?
(OPTIONAL THEME: ADVERSITY)

1. _____

2. _____

3. _____

WHAT MESSAGE DO I NEED TO REMIND MYSELF OF TODAY?

HOW CAN I CHANGE MY MINDSET TO ATTRACT THE LIFE I TRULY WANT?

IF I LOOKED AT MYSELF FROM THE PERSPECTIVE OF A CARE-GIVER, HOW WOULD I GUIDE MYSELF TO HAPPINESS?

MINI GRATITUDE ACTION OF THE DAY:

Completed?

AVOID COMPLAINING ALL DAY TODAY. EACH TIME YOUR NEGATIVE SIDE COMES OUT, ACKNOWLEDGE IT AND SEND IT ON ITS WAY. NOTICE HOW YOU FEEL AT THE END OF THE DAY. EXHAUSTED? HAPPIER? WHY IS THAT?

163

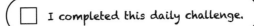

Day 56: **Daily Challenge** ♦

Challenge: Try this gratitude meditation.

We all know how difficult it can be to try and stay positive when feeling distraught and overwhelmed by difficult life circumstances. As we've been sharing throughout this journal, the aim isn't to ignore the 'bad' and focus on the 'good,' but rather to find an appreciation for the 'bad,' through altering one's perspective.

1. Find a quiet room where you won't be disturbed.
2. Sit on a chair or cushion.
3. Set a timer for anywhere from 5-10 minutes.
4. Take 10 breaths as you try to relax any tension in your body.
5. Bring your attention to something in your life that you're having a difficult time with. Begin with small irritations.
6. See if you can flip your perspective on this annoyance to find something positive in it.
7. Once you've brought something up, seen it from a different perspective, move onto something else you feel unhappy about in your life.
8. Repeat the exercise for the allotted amount of time.

This isn't easy to do, but there is no better time to think and try to see one's own circumstances from a different point of view than in the quiet, alone with oneself.

☐ I completed this daily challenge.

I am a part of something special. I collaborate with others at work, as a parent, as a member of society and this is the essence of living life.

WHAT AM I GRATEFUL FOR TODAY?
(OPTIONAL THEME: RELATIONSHIPS)

1. _____

2. _____

3. _____

WHAT MESSAGE DO I NEED TO REMIND MYSELF OF TODAY?

_____

_____

_____

IN WHAT WAYS COULD I BE WAY LESS FORTUNATE THAN I AM NOW?

_____

_____

_____

HOW COULD I SHIFT MY SELF-TALK TO BE MUCH MORE SUPPORTIVE, AS IF I WERE MY OWN BEST FRIEND?

_____

_____

MINI GRATITUDE ACTION OF THE DAY:

Completed?

BUY SOMEONE (EVEN YOURSELF!) SOME FLOWERS. ENJOY THEM WHENEVER YOU LOOK AT THEM AND LOOK AT THE JOURNEY THEY WENT THROUGH TO GROW, SPROUT, AND NOW BRING BEAUTY INTO THIS WORLD!

☐

Day 57: **Pro-Tip**

When you say 'thank you,' mean it.

When we're kids, as soon as we're able to talk, one of the first things we learn from our parents and society is to say 'thank you' as a response to basically anything another person does for us.

Repeating the words 'thank you' very quickly becomes an automatic response to receiving anything from another person. The words just fly out of our mouths. We don't even give it a thought, it simply happens.

We all also know what it feels like to be genuinely grateful for something from another person. We know the drastic difference in saying thank you as an automatic response vs. saying thank you and actually feeling grateful for what you've received.

Practicing gratitude isn't about appearing positive to the outside world - it's about experiencing the awesome feeling of it. The feeling is what transcends your attitude, not the outward expression of it.

See if you can make a practice of feeling grateful whenever you say thank you. It's one of the best reminders to FEEL grateful throughout the day.

"To know oneself is to study oneself in action with another person."
- Bruce Lee

166

I sit in my sadness and do not try to push it away. I know that my brain and body need to process my emotions and I do not try to push myself through_____ them. I am entitled to all of my emotions.

DATE

♡ WHAT AM I GRATEFUL FOR TODAY?
(OPTIONAL THEME: EVERY-DAY THINGS)

1. _____

2. _____

3. _____

WHAT MESSAGE DO I NEED TO REMIND MYSELF OF TODAY?

_____

_____

_____

WHAT AM I TAKING FOR GRANTED IN MY LIFE?

_____

_____

_____

WHAT'S SOMETHING I DID THAT I STILL REGRET? HOW CAN I EMPATHIZE WITH MYSELF FOR IT AND LEARN FROM IT INSTEAD?

_____

_____

MINI GRATITUDE ACTION OF THE DAY:

Completed?

THINK OF A PAST RELATIONSHIP YOU HAD WITH SOMEONE - REGARDLESS OF WHETHER OR NOT THEY'RE STILL IN YOUR LIFE, WHAT CAN YOU APPRECIATE FROM IT?

☐

Day 58: **Recommended Resource** ¶¶

**Watch Shawn Achor's TedX Talk on rewiring your brain.**

This 12-minute talk from positive psychologist Shawn Achor is extremely popular because of Achor's use of humor throughout. In the talk, Achor starts out by discussing a story from his childhood involving his little sister, which underlines the importance of seeing the positive side of everything.

He's hilarious, and brings light to the importance of perspective - how your view of the world shapes your reality. Only 10% of your happiness level is linked to your external circumstances. 90% is based on what you're experiencing inside. _**What you're experiencing inside is based on how you interpret the events of your life.**_

By the end of the talk, Achor has laid out a plan for everyone to rewire their brains to recognize the positive before the negative, starting with recognizing things they are grateful for. This funny, actionable talk is a must-watch.

You can check out the talk by searching 'Shawn Achor TedX Talk' on YouTube or the TED app.

HAPPINESS ADVANTAGE

"If you concentrate on finding whatever is good in every situation, you will discover that your life will suddenly be filled with gratitude, a feeling that nurtures the soul." - Rabbi Harold Kushner

. I acknowledge that fighting with friends and family is normal. I acknowledge that in the midst of these struggles, I am still loved.

DATE

WHAT AM I GRATEFUL FOR TODAY?
(OPTIONAL THEME: MY BODY)

1. _____

2. _____

3. _____

WHAT MESSAGE DO I NEED TO REMIND MYSELF OF TODAY?

_____

_____

_____

KNOWING WHAT I KNOW TODAY, HOW WOULD I GUIDE MY YOUNGER SELF THROUGH A DIFFICULT SITUATION I WENT THROUGH?

_____

_____

_____

HOW COULD I BE MORE SUPPORTIVE OF MYSELF?

_____

_____

MINI GRATITUDE ACTION OF THE DAY:

Completed?

THE NEXT TIME YOU HAVE A MEAL, REALLY THINK OF THE WHOLE CHAIN OF EVENTS THAT LED TO HAVING THAT PIECE OF FOOD APPEAR ON YOUR PLATE.

Day 59: **Pro-Tip**

Create a reference point of gratitude for yourself.

Spend a few dedicated minutes right now, tapping into your heart's **deepest** levels of gratitude. Pull out every idea of what you can be thankful for - your health, your talents, your family, your connections... everything. Realize how truly lucky you are and take yourself to that point of deep gratitude. **Do this now.**

Afterwards, write down everything you experienced and may still be experiencing. Write about how you feel, what your view towards the world is, where your mind is.

Now... how do you feel about the gift of life?

Know that you just took yourself to this beautiful state, and that this is the emotional benchmark of how you can feel. Set this as a baseline of gratitude that you want to live up to. Maybe not every day, not every moment, but use this as a realization of the true extent of how you can feel and exist in this world.

The next time you are having an AVERAGE day, not even a terrible one, revisit this note. Any day you aren't realizing the potential you have in this world, revisit what you wrote.

Don't even force yourself to change into that blissfully mindful state, just use it as a reference point of what's possible, of how you can feel... the beauty of the fact that a series of events can lead you there.

"Gratitude makes sense of our past, brings peace for today, and creates a vision for tomorrow." - Melody Beattie

I am a lifelong learner. I know the value of being open-minded to the world around me.

WHAT AM I GRATEFUL FOR TODAY?
(OPTIONAL THEME: COINCIDENCES)

1. _____

2. _____

3. _____

WHAT MESSAGE DO I NEED TO REMIND MYSELF OF TODAY?

_____

_____

_____

HOW DO I UTILIZE MY TALENTS AND ABILITIES IN WAYS I DON'T THINK ABOUT OR FULLY APPRECIATE?

_____

_____

_____

WHAT CAN I FORGIVE MYSELF FOR?

_____

_____

MINI GRATITUDE ACTION OF THE DAY:

Completed?

WEAR YOUR FAVORITE OUTFIT TODAY. THINK ABOUT WHAT MAKES IT YOUR FAVORITE AND FEEL GRATITUDE FOR THE PEOPLE WHO DESIGNED IT, MADE THE FABRIC, SEWED IT TOGETHER, SHIPPED IT, UNPACKED IT, AND SOLD IT TO YOU.

Day 60: **Pro-Tip** 💡

<u>Ready to work towards a new habit goal?</u>

Heads up: you're on the final pages of this journal!

If you've gotten this far, you've had a strong taste of how drastically intentional gratitude can impact the quality of my emotions.

Everything we do impacts the quality of our thoughts and emotions. That includes the food we eat, whether or not we exercise regularly, how much we sleep, whether we make good use of our time, etc.

It would be wise to begin thinking more about your lifestyle habits in general and how some changes to your everyday habits could improve the quality of your gratitude practice, as well as your overall quality of life!

These are the other habit journals we offer:

- *The Morning Sidekick Journal*
- *The Nutrition & Weight Management Sidekick Journal*
- *The Meditation Sidekick Journal*
- *The Badass Body Goals Fitness Journal*
- *The Weightlifting Gym Buddy*

Note: get a sneak peek of these after day 66 of this journal.

"Know that you are your greatest enemy, but also your greatest friend."
- Jeremy Taylor

I am a voice for the voiceless. I recognize my ability to advocate for others and I take the opportunity to do so.

WHAT AM I GRATEFUL FOR TODAY?
(OPTIONAL THEME: WORK-RELATED)

1. _____

2. _____

3. _____

WHAT MESSAGE DO I NEED TO REMIND MYSELF OF TODAY?

_____

_____

_____

WHAT AM I HOLDING ONTO FROM MY PAST THAT IS HOLDING ME BACK?

_____

_____

_____

IN WHAT WAYS DOES THINKING ABOUT THE PAST STOP ME FROM IMPROVING IN THE FUTURE?

_____

_____

MINI GRATITUDE ACTION OF THE DAY:

Completed?

WATCH THE SUN SET TONIGHT. EVEN IF IT IS A CLOUDY DAY, APPRECIATE THE TRANSITION FROM DAY TO NIGHT, ACKNOWLEDGING THAT NOTHING, NOT GOOD, NOT BAD, NOT MEDIOCRE, LASTS FOREVER.

173

Day 61: **Affirmations**

1. Find a quiet area where you can do this in private so you can be at ease. If you can't find a private space, say this in your head while pretending you're screaming it from a mountaintop.

2. Think of a time when you felt absolutely powerful - **when you felt on top of the world**. Tap into every emotion you had at that moment and get yourself into that state right now. How were you feeling then - Powerful? Unstoppable? Strong? Incredible!? Get into it now!!!!

3. Now feel your intensity grow tenfold! Say this with deep passion:

Each morning is a miracle. My heart beats, my lungs breathe, my limbs move, my mind thinks without asking for anything in return. This experience of life is a mystery of wonder and I express my gratitude in the way I choose to live my life.

Repeat this **one more time.**

"As we express our gratitude, we must never forget that the highest appreciation is not to utter words, but to live by them." - John F. Kennedy

I am responsible for the things I say. I
recognize that sometimes I may need to
apologize, even if I felt justified in my words.

WHAT AM I GRATEFUL FOR TODAY?
(OPTIONAL THEME: NATURE)

1. _____

2. _____

3. _____

WHAT MESSAGE DO I NEED TO REMIND MYSELF OF TODAY?

_____

_____

_____

**DOES REACTING NEGATIVELY EVER HELP A SITUATION I HAVE NO CHOICE
BUT TO DEAL WITH? HOW CAN I SHIFT MY VIEW ON THINGS INSTEAD?**

_____

_____

_____

HOW DOES MY MIND EXAGGERATE THE NEGATIVE WAYS I VIEW MYSELF?

_____

_____

MINI GRATITUDE ACTION OF THE DAY:

Completed?

WHEN YOU CLIMB INTO BED TONIGHT, RELISH THE COMFORT OF YOUR PILLOW
AND BLANKETS, THAT YOU HAVE A PLACE TO FEEL COMFORTABLE.

☐

Day 62: **Pro-Tip**

Schedule gratitude moments.

No matter where you are on this journey of incorporating more gratitude into your life, we always need to have ways of reminding ourselves to bring our attention back to what we have to be grateful for. It can take a long time for our brains to really adapt to automatically incorporating gratefulness into our perspective, and setting reminders for ourselves is a necessary aspect of that process.

That's what the gratitude jar is about, that's what the gratitude board is about, that's what this journal is about!

Another tip you can try is literally choosing 2-3 times throughout your day in which you'll stop what you're doing and simply remember to find that feeling of appreciation for absolutely anything (or even without having it attached to anything at all).

Set up reminders in your phone and write yourself a nice gentle message, nudging you to take just a minute or two to find the feeling of gratitude.

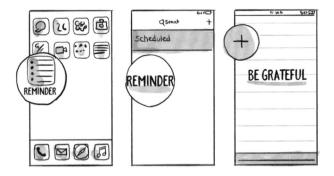

"I looked around and thought about my life. I felt grateful. I noticed every detail. That is the key to time travel. You can only move if you are actually in the moment. You have to be where you are to get where you need to go." - Amy Poehler

I am connected to everyone. My actions, big or small, can affect not only people around me, but the people around them, on and on.

WHAT AM I GRATEFUL FOR TODAY?
(OPTIONAL THEME: OPPORTUNITIES)

1. _____

2. _____

3. _____

WHAT MESSAGE DO I NEED TO REMIND MYSELF OF TODAY?

_____

_____

_____

WHAT BIG LIFE EVENT OR GOAL IS MY HAPPINESS ATTACHED TO?

_____

_____

_____

HOW CAN I TAKE MORE RESPONSIBILITY FOR MY OWN EMOTIONS AND BLAME OTHER PEOPLE OR EXTERNAL CIRCUMSTANCES LESS?

_____

_____

MINI GRATITUDE ACTION OF THE DAY:

Completed?

TOMORROW MORNING MAKE IT A GOAL TO IMMEDIATELY BE THANKFUL OF SOMETHING AS THE FIRST THOUGHT YOU HAVE WHEN YOU WAKE UP!

☐

177

Day 63: **Affirmations**

1. Find a quiet area where you can do this in private so you can be at ease. If you can't find a private space, say this in your head while pretending you're screaming it from a mountaintop.

2. Think of a time when you felt absolutely powerful - **when you felt on top of the world**. Tap into every emotion you had at that moment and get yourself into that state right now. How were you feeling then - Powerful? Unstoppable? Strong? Incredible!? Get into it now!!!!

3. Now feel your intensity grow tenfold! Say this with deep passion:

I am exited for others in their successes and celebrate with them wholeheartedly. I know that surrounding myself with success will only further breed my own success. I attract potential, prosperity, and achievement because I am open and secure in myself.

Repeat this **one more time.**

"Fear comes from uncertainty; we can eliminate the fear within us when we know ourselves better." - Bruce Lee

178

I accept that I do not have the ultimate control. I will release the reigns on feeling that I, alone, have the ability to change others. I can only change myself.

WHAT AM I GRATEFUL FOR TODAY?
(OPTIONAL THEME: MY OWN TALENTS & ABILITIES)

1. _____

2. _____

3. _____

WHAT MESSAGE DO I NEED TO REMIND MYSELF OF TODAY?

_____

_____

_____

IN WHAT WAYS DO MY PRECONCEIVED IDEAS OF WHO PEOPLE ARE AFFECT MY RELATIONSHIPS?

_____

_____

_____

HOW CAN I REMOVE GUILT FROM MY LIFE?

_____

_____

MINI GRATITUDE ACTION OF THE DAY:

Completed?

THE NEXT TIME YOU SEE AN ANIMAL TODAY, THINK OF HOW THEY CONTRIBUTE TO THIS WORLD. HOW DOES THAT CONTINUE EVEN AFTER YOU SEE THEM?

179

Day 64: **Daily Challenge** 🔥

**Challenge: Try to be as non-judgmental as possible for an entire day.**

Perception is dependent on how we bring attention to the people, events, and circumstances of our lives.

Something we all have inside of us is this almost constant tendency to judge. Following judgment comes blame or criticism. Following blame or criticism comes resentment or guilt.

When you're judging, blaming, criticizing or resenting anything about yourself, another person, or any situation you're confronted with, there is no space for gratitude.

The challenge is to be as non-judgmental as possible for an entire day. What that means, is as soon as you notice the thoughts in your head being judgmental, you immediately let go of it and recognize it as an automatic response of your mind to what's happening.

The more you do this, the more you create space for something new to enter your perspective. You are LITERALLY creating the space to feel grateful.

☐ I completed this daily challenge.

"Whenever you feel like criticizing any one...just remember that all the people in this world haven't had the advantages that you've had.."
- F. Scott Fitzgerald

I love myself the way I want others to love me. I do not put myself down or make myself feel lesser.

WHAT AM I GRATEFUL FOR TODAY?
(OPTIONAL THEME: EXPERIENCES)

1. _____
2. _____
3. _____

WHAT MESSAGE DO I NEED TO REMIND MYSELF OF TODAY?

_____

_____

_____

WHAT EXPERIENCE AM I GRATEFUL FOR, BUT AM GLAD IT IS OVER?

_____

_____

_____

WHY DO I JUDGE MYSELF SO HARSHLY?

_____

_____

MINI GRATITUDE ACTION OF THE DAY:

Completed?

REFLECT ON WHAT GIVES YOU PURPOSE IN LIFE. SIT IN THAT FEELING OF PURPOSE AND LET IT ENVELOP YOU, GIVE YOU A FEELING OF ENERGY AND LIFE.

☐

181

Day 65: **Recommended Resource** 🍴

Watch Brian Doyle's 365 Days of Thank You TedX Talk.

Brian Doyle is a young man who is passionate about collecting stories and helping others through the power of ideas.

After a really bad car accident, Brian found himself extremely grateful for his life, and he wondered, why now? Why am I not grateful more often?

So he set out on a journey of saying thank you to a different person for 365 days.

Number 170 on his list was his father. When the day came to thank his father, he found himself extremely nervous. His heart was pounding out of his chest, and he again wondered, why? Why did telling his father how much he appreciated him make him so nervous?

It's a story worth listening to, and it's only 8 minutes long.

Check out Brian's TedX talk by searching 'Brian Doyle TedX Talk' on YouTube or the TED app!

"Gratitude is the healthiest of all human emotions. The more you express gratitude for what you have, the more likely you will have even more to express gratitude for.." - Zig Ziglar

I have everything I need to be happy, every moment and every second of my life. My happiness is directly tied to my perspective.

DATE

WHAT AM I GRATEFUL FOR TODAY?
(OPTIONAL THEME: TECHNOLOGY)

1. _____
2. _____
3. _____

WHAT MESSAGE DO I NEED TO REMIND MYSELF OF TODAY?

_____

_____

_____

WHAT WAS THE LAST NICE THING I DID FOR SOMEBODY?

_____

_____

_____

WHAT 'WRONG' CAN I 'RIGHT' WITH THE HELP OF GRATITUDE?

_____

_____

MINI GRATITUDE ACTION OF THE DAY:

Completed?

FIND ONE SPOT IN YOUR HOME THAT IS CLUTTERED AND MAKE IT A POINT TO DECLUTTER IT TODAY. NOTICE HOW MUCH MORE YOU ENJOY THAT SPOT NOW THAN WHEN IT WAS AN EYESORE.

183

Day 66: **Congratulations!!!** 🥂

You've made it to the end of the journal. **You are a Gratitude Warrior!**

For you to have gotten this far means you've earned a very serious congratulations. You need to celebrate because your willpower and confidence should be soaring through the roof. You've gained lessons about yourself not many dare to approach. You've struggled with your own mind, and gained some serious control over your outlook. You're much closer to understanding that the quality of your emotional life is dependent on your perspective, and that you can change your perspective to better fit what you want to experience.

This is a skill you've built inside you that you can turn on whenever you need it at any future point in your lifetime. **That's so awesome.**

You are a WARRIOR and we (Amir, Ari, & Mikey) hope you continue to build on your habit success and personal development for the rest of your life.

"If the only prayer you said in your whole life was "thank you," that would suffice."- Meister Eckhart

I allow myself to receive. I am deserving of all of the goodness I have and will have. I do not feel guilt for being blessed with life.

WHAT AM I GRATEFUL FOR TODAY?
(OPTIONAL THEME: ADVERSITY)

1. _____

2. _____

3. _____

WHAT MESSAGE DO I NEED TO REMIND MYSELF OF TODAY?

_____

_____

_____

HOW CAN I CHANGE MY MINDSET TO ATTRACT THE LIFE I TRULY WANT?

_____

_____

_____

IF I LOOKED AT MYSELF FROM THE PERSPECTIVE OF A CARE-GIVER, HOW WOULD I GUIDE MYSELF TO HAPPINESS?

_____

_____

 MINI GRATITUDE ACTION OF THE DAY:

Completed?

FIND AN OPPORTUNITY TO TRULY LAUGH TODAY. LISTEN OR WATCH A STAND-UP COMEDIAN, CALL YOUR FUNNY FRIEND, LOOK THROUGH AN OLD YEARBOOK AND HAVE A GOOD CHUCKLE!

☐

185

~~PHASE 3.~~

MASTERED.

Phase 3 Recap: Days 22-66+

1. What are the most important experiences I've had since beginning the journal?

_____

_____

_____

_____

2. How has gratitude changed my life since beginning this journey?

_____

_____

_____

_____

3. How do I plan on continuing to practice gratitude in the future?

_____

_____

_____

4. What have I learned about myself?

_____

_____

- Fin -

So... What Now?

Although you should feel very accomplished for getting through this entire journal... know that you built this habit to *continually improve your life. Don't stop now. This is only the beginning.*

One huge factor to this is tracking your progress. Once you stop tracking, it makes it exponentially easier for you to skip having a productive morning (due to the lack of accountability with yourself).

Remember: **Every single day in your life where you start your morning with focus, intent, and energy will automatically be a better day of your life.**

You only stand to gain from continuing this habit.

Meet the Habit Nest Team

Amir Atighehchi graduated from USC's Marshall School of Business in 2013. He got his first taste of entrepreneurship during college with Mikey when they co-founded a bicycle lock company called *Nutlock*. It wasn't until after college when he opened his eyes to the world of personal development and healthy habits. Amir is fascinated by creative challenges and entrepreneurship.

Mikey Ahdoot transformed his life from a 200+ pound video game addict to someone who was completing 17 daily habits consistently at one point. From ice cold showers to brainstorming 10 ideas a day (shoutout to James Altucher) to celebrating life every single day, he is first-hand becoming a habit routine machine that sets himself up for success daily. He is a graduate of USC's Marshall School of Business and a proud Trojan.

Ari Banayan graduated from the University of Southern California Gould School of Law in 2016. Through his own life experience, he understands how important it is to take care of ourselves mentally, physically and emotionally to operate at maximum capacity. He uses waking up early, reading, meditation, exercise, and a healthy diet to create a solid foundation for his everyday life.

Read all of our full stories here:

habitnest.com/about-us

Shop Habit Nest Products

Morning Sidekick
Journal

The Morning Sidekick Journal is the first journal we created at Habit Nest. It consists of 66 days of content and 66 days of tracking.

Morning routines are shown to be one of the most **critical elements of winning your day.** Starting your day off on the right foot sets the tone for the rest of it.

The journal is specifically designed to **create a cycle of accountability** within yourself by using your nights to hold you accountable in the morning, and your mornings to map out what's needed for that night.

It's jam-packed with effective and actionable content that will help you build this habit in bite sized chunks.

Like all of our products, the *Morning Sidekick Journal* comes with a 50-year satisfaction guarantee.

One thing we love: Regardless of what time you wake up, the journal will show you how to create a routine (short or long) that works for you.

Get yours at **habitnest.com/morning**

Sample Journal Page

ight 0

Begin
ghttime
utine.)

TONIGHT I'LL SLEEP AT: __11:30pm__ & TOMORROW I'LL WAKE UP AT: __6:30am__

✺ MEMORABLE MOMENT(S) I EXPERIENCED TODAY:

Watching the sunrise on my morning run :)

Finally made progress on my side-business!

☀ MY MORNING RITUAL TOMORROW WILL BE:

Completed?

1. __5 minutes of meditation__ ☑

2. __Read 2 pages of "Think and Grow Rich"__ ☑

3. __Affirmations__ ☐

4. __Walk 2 blocks outside__ ☐

5. __Plan out and strategize the rest of my day__ ☐

Day 1

Begin
orning
utine.)

LAST NIGHT I SLEPT AT: __12am__ & WOKE UP TODAY AT: __7am__

🐎 MY MOST IMPORTANT TASK FOR TODAY IS:

Begin designing the app for my new startup

⊕ ONE WAY I CAN IMPROVE LIFE BY 1% IS:

Less Facebook / Instagram in the mornings

🧘 TOP TWO DISTRACTIONS TO MINIMIZE TONIGHT (BEFORE BED):

1. Watching YouTube in bed (limit: 15mins)

2. Watching the news (limit: 15mins)

Meditation Sidekick
J o u r n a l

The Meditation Sidekick Journal is built to help two types of people:

1. To help **newcomers or past strugglers** to easily own the practice of meditation.

2. To help **constant meditators** push their practice to another level.

Layout of the Journal

1. **Building the foundation** - get a quick insight into the *science behind meditation* and clarity of what you're likely to experience during it.

2. **Accountability** - track your practice daily to see your progress and hold yourself accountable in staying consistent.

3. **Learn in bite-sized chunks** - get daily exposure to different types of meditations (i.e. transcendental, gratitude, physical body, etc.) and see which ones impact your life the most.

One thing we love: The journal is not just designed to help you meditate effectively, but more importantly, to **help you reach the end goal of consistently living mindfully every day.**

Get yours at **habitnest.com/meditation**

Sample Journal Page

 TODAY I WILL MEDITATE AT:

 FOR AT LEAST:

7:30 a.m. ✓

5 minutes ✓

 ONE UPCOMING MENTAL OR EMOTIONAL HURDLE TO BE MINDFUL OF:

My presentation for my boss at work – own it!

BENEFITS I FELT TODAY (CIRCLE):

Feel Happier | More Creative | Increased | Improved Focus | More Energized | Reduced Stress

 WHAT DOES MY INTERNAL DIALOGUE CONSIST OF?

I realize that I think about my appearance A LOT…
and I immediately assume people judge me for it.

 ONE SMALL WAY I CAN IMPROVE MY INTERNAL DIALOGUE:

I could be more understanding when I'm feeling self-conscious and willingly accept myself for how I look.

OPENING UP ABOUT MY DAY:

Today was a rollercoaster. I realize that when I'm working with others, I prefer not to rely on them to get things done. It's something I want to work on improving because I make myself feel anxious when it happens.

Nutrition Sidekick
Journal

The Nutrition Sidekick Journal has a similar layout to *The Morning Sidekick Journal.* It's designed to be flexible and adaptable to whatever food goals you may have. It can be used to successfully implement:

- Calorie counting
- Weight management and/or muscle building
- General healthy eating
- Paleo / vegan / IIFYM / ketosis / other custom diets

The journal serves as your personal trainer for losing weight and **regaining control over your eating habits** quickly and effectively.

It allows you to **perfectly track** all that you need for YOUR body's optimum nutrition. These include:

- Daily caloric intake goal
- Water drinking goal
- Exercise goal
- Planned vs. actual meals, (& caloric intake for each)
- Snacks, alcohol, and other intake
- Upcoming big meals to watch out for

One thing we love: A lot of the tips are designed to help you **break the association** that may exist between **your confidence / happiness** and **your body weight.**

Get yours at **habitnest.com/nutrition**

Sample Journal Page

⊕ **TODAY'S NUTRITION GOAL**

_____ DATE

2,100 calories ☑

💧 **WATER DRINKING GOAL**   🚶 **EXERCISE GOAL**

Two 500mL bottles ☑   2 mile jog ☐

🍽 **TODAY'S MEALS**

📅 Planned	✓ Actual	Calories	Protein / Carbs / Fat
eggs w/ 2 rice cakes	3 eggs w/ 2 rice cakes	340	18g
Chicken + Broccoli + cauliflower	Burrito (tortilla, avocado, tomatoes, chicken)	800	1.5g
almon w/ asparagus	Salmon w/ asparagus	500	51g

🍎 SNACKS, DRINKS, & OTHER

30 almonds	210	9g
One snickerdoodle cookie	250	2.5g

TODAY'S TOTALS: __2,100__ __82g__ _____

 POTENTIAL FOOD OBSTACLE(S) TO LOOK OUT FOR TOMORROW:

Resist the cookies at lunch!

⊕ **ONE SMALL WAY I CAN IMPROVE MY NUTRITION TOMORROW IS:**

If I bring a snack to work, I can eat that instead of sweets.

The Weightlifting Gym Buddy

Journal

The Weightlifting Gym Buddy Journal is a complete 12-week personal training program.

No thinking required, just open the journal, follow the workouts, and track your progress. The journal is designed to accompany you to the gym, to help you track your weight/reps for each workout, and to help you compete against yourself every workout.

- **Contains 60 guided workouts for you to follow**

- **Each day's workout targets 2 muscle groups**

- **For lifters of all levels to push themselves to the next level and maximize competition with themselves**

- **Each workout takes 45-60 minutes**

- **Number of reps to aim for is already set for you**

- **Built with a pyramid weight/rep format to intensify each exercise dramatically**

- **No thinking required - just open the journal and follow along for amazing results**

- **Alternative exercises are listed in the case your gym is missing a specific machine**

Get yours at <u>habitnest.com/weightlifting</u>

(You'll see links to exercise guides here each day)

Sample Workout: Biceps & Triceps

DATE _____

1. PREACHER CURL

ALTERNATIVE: SEATED DUMBBELL CURL)

PREVIOUS BEST   REPS: ___5___   WEIGHT: ___60___

SET 1   REPS: ___14___   (GOAL: 10-15)   WEIGHT: ___40___
SET 2   REPS: ___10___   (GOAL: 8-12)   WEIGHT: ___50___
SET 3   REPS: ___7___   (GOAL: 6-8)   WEIGHT: ___60___
SET 4   REPS: ___6___   (GOAL: 4-6)   WEIGHT: ___60___
(OPTIONAL)

CLOSE GRIP BENCH PRESS

(By having your "Previous Best" reps and weight values listed for each specific exercise, you'll have a clear target to beat weekly.)

PREVIOUS BEST   REPS: ___5___   WEIGHT: ___50___

SET 1   REPS: ___13___   (GOAL: 10-15)   WEIGHT: ___30___
SET 2   REPS: ___10___   (GOAL: 8-12)   WEIGHT: ___40___
SET 3   REPS: ___8___   (GOAL: 6-8)   WEIGHT: ___50___
SET 4   REPS: ___5___   (GOAL: 4-6)   WEIGHT: ___50___
(OPTIONAL)

3. ROPE HAMMER CURL

(The fourth set on each exercise is optional but highly recommended.)

PREVIOUS BEST   REPS: ___6___   WEIGHT: ___50___

SET 1   REPS: ___11___   (GOAL: 10-15)   WEIGHT: ___35___
SET 2   REPS: ___11___   (GOAL: 8-12)   WEIGHT: ___45___
SET 3   REPS: ___7___   (GOAL: 6-8)   WEIGHT: ___50___
SET 4   REPS: ___-___   (GOAL: 4-6)   WEIGHT: ___-___
(OPTIONAL)

4. OVERHEAD DUMBBELL EXTENSION

PREVIOUS BEST   REPS: ___4___   WEIGHT: ___55___

SET 1   REPS: ___14___   (GOAL: 10-15)   WEIGHT: ___35___
SET 2   REPS: ___12___   (GOAL: 8-12)   WEIGHT: ___45___
SET 3   REPS: ___6___   (GOAL: 6-8)   WEIGHT: ___45___
SET 4   REPS: ___5___   (GOAL: 4-6)   WEIGHT: ___55___
(OPTIONAL)

 TODAY'S WORKOUT INTENSITY: _____ / 10

The Badass Body Goals
Booty Shaping &
Resistance Training
Journal

The Badass Body Goals Booty Shaping & Resistance Training Journal is a full 10-week personal training program which includes 50 guided workouts that are each unique, engaging, and challenging.

The journal is co-written by fitness expert Jennifer Cohen and has a large focus on circuit training (60% of the journal) with a variety of weight training for the remainder.

- The journal is designed to be done at home or in the gym with weights if you want to use more resistance.

- Every journal comes with a timed video guide that allows you to do the workout from beginning to end by simply following along each day.

- Track your results by filling in certain important variables as you complete each workout. As a result, you'll be getting constant encouragement by seeing first-hand how quickly you're improving.

- The journal contains an optimal mix of 4-3-2-1 interval circuits and resistance training workouts workout days. The two are designed to keep you engaged with different movements for short periods which will optimize fat loss and muscle development at the same time.

Get yours at **habitnest.com/badass**

<u>Workout 1: 4-3-2-1</u>

 30s EACH <u>GLUTE ACTIVATION WARMUP</u>

a. Clam Opener

b. Glute Bridge w/ Band Flutter

c. Fire Hydrant

d. Lateral Leg Raise

(30s Each Leg)

(30s Each Side)

- 30s Each Leg (w/ Foot Flexed)
- 30s Each Leg (w/ Toes Pointing Down)

——— 30 SECOND BREAK ———

60s EACH <u>**CIRCUIT 1**</u>

1a. Curtsy Lunge

1b. Curtsy Lunge

1c. Boxing Jab

1d. Side to Side Squat

PS: _____

(Left Leg)

→ REPS: _____

(Right Leg)

→ REPS: _____

→ REPS: _____

——— 30 SECOND BREAK ———

50s EACH <u>**CIRCUIT 2**</u>

a. 180° Jump Twist to Floor Tap

2b. Squat to Overhead Press

2c. Plie Jump Squat

SET 1 REPS: _____

SET 2 REPS: _____

→

→

SET 1 REPS: _____

SET 2 REPS: _____

→

→

SET 1 REPS: _____

SET 2 REPS: _____

Share The Love

If you're reading this, that means you've come pretty far from where you were when starting. You should be extremely proud of yourself!

If you believe this journal has had a positive impact on your life, we invite you to consider gifting a new one to a friend.

Is there a holiday coming up? Is there a special birthday around the corner? Or do you just want to put a smile on someone's face and do something incredible for them?

Gifting this journal is the absolute best way to show any gratitude you may have for what we've written here, as well as serving as a force of good through giving back to others. And you can rest assured that you're helping improve another person's life at the same time.

We created a discount code for getting this far that can be used for any Gratitude Sidekick Journal reorder (make sure to use the same email address you placed the order with).

If you decide to, feel free to re-order here:
habitnest.com/gratitude

Use code **GiveGratitude** for 15% off!

Content Index

How Was This Journal Created?

We formulated the journal as a mix between what we find personally effective through our own experience as well as through researching published scientific material and books on the newest, most relevant information we could find.

The following is a mix of studies we used to formulate the journal - some points take ideas found in some sources and mix them with our own experience or with other research points.

Some of the main sources of inspiration came from:

It is a bit difficult to assign specific studies to specific pages in the book as there is a decent amount of overlap in different sections, though we will do our best.

The 'Why'

Fishbach, Ayelet, and Ravi Dhar. "Goals as Excuses or Guides: The Liberating Effect of Perceived Goal Progress on Choice." Journal of Consumer Research, vol. 32, no. 3, 2005, pp. 370–377., doi:10.1086/497548.

The 'Who'

Clear, James. Atomic Habits. Avery, 2018. pp. 30-34.

Feeling bad makes cake look good: Chun, H., V. M. Patrick, and D. J. MacInnis. "Making Prudent Vs. Impulsive Choices: The Role of Anticipated Shame and Guilt on Consumer Self-Control." Advances in Consumer Research 34 (2007): 715–19.

The what-the-hell effect: Polivy, J., and C. P. Herman. "Dieting and Binging: A Causal Analysis." American Psychologist 40 (1985): 193–201. See also guilt survey: Steenhuis, I. "Guilty or Not? Feelings of Guilt About Food Among College Women." Appetite 52 (2009): 531–34

The 'What'

Gardner, Benjamin, et al. "Making Health Habitual: the Psychology of 'Habit-Formation' and General Practice." British Journal of General Practice, vol. 62, no. 605, 2012, pp. 664–666., doi:10.3399/bjgp12x659466.

The 'How'

Tangney, June P., et al. "High Self-Control Predicts Good Adjustment, Less Pathology, Better Grades, and Interpersonal Success." Journal of Personality, vol. 72, no. 2, 2004, pp. 271–324., doi:10.1111/j.0022-3506.2004.00263.x.

Tracking Pages

Fishbach, Ayelet, and Ravi Dhar. "Goals as Excuses or Guides: The Liberating Effect of Perceived Goal Progress on Choice." Journal of Consumer Research, vol. 32, no. 3, 2005, pp. 370–377., doi:10.1086/497548.

Fogg, BJ. "What Causes Behavior Change?" BJ Fogg's Behavior Model, www.behaviormodel.org/index.html.

Throughout the Journal

Summer Allen, Ph.D., "The Science of Gratitude", a white paper prepared for the John Templeton Foundation by the Greater Good Science Center at UC Berkeley, https://ggsc.berkeley.edu/images/uploads/GGSC-JTF_White_Paper-Gratitude-FINAL.pdf

Robert A. Emmons and Michael E. McCullough, "Counting Blessings Versus Burdens: An Experimental Investigation of Gratitude and Subjective Well-Being in Daily Life," 2003, Journal of Personality and Social Psychology, https://greatergood.berkeley.edu/pdfs/GratitudePDFs/6Emmons-BlessingsBurdens.pdf

Jordan Paul LaBouff, Wade C. Rowatt, Megan K. Johnson, Jo-Ann Tsang & Grace McCullough Willerton (2012) Humble persons are more helpful than less humble persons: Evidence from three studies, The Journal of Positive Psychology, 7:1, 16-29, DOI: 10.1080/17439760.2011.626787
Robert A. Emmons and Cheryl A. Crumpler (2000). Gratitude as a Human Strength: Appraising the Evidence. Journal of Social and Clinical Psychology: Vol. 19, No. 1, pp. 56-69. https://doi.org/10.1521/jscp.2000.19.1.56

Froh, J.J., Emmons, R.A., Card, N.A. et al. J Happiness Stud (2011) 12: 289. https://doi.org/10.1007/s10902-010-9195-9

Killen, A. & Macaskill, A. J Happiness Stud (2015) 16: 947. https://doi.org/10.1007/s10902-014-9542-3

Philip C. Watkins, Kathrane Woodward, Tamara Stone, Russell L. Kolts, "Gratitude and Happiness: Development of A Measure of Gratitude, and Relationships With Subjective Well-Being," Social Behavior and Personality: an international journal, Volume 31, Number 5, 2003, pp. 431-451(21), https://doi.org/10.2224/sbp.2003.31.5.431